THE ANTIOXIDANT RECIPE BOOK

Also available:

THE ANTIOXIDANT HEALTH PLAN
Dr Robert Youngson

THE
ANTIOXIDANT RECIPE BOOK

Amanda Ursell

Thorsons
An Imprint of HarperCollins*Publishers*

Thorsons
An Imprint of HarperCollinsPublishers
77-85 Fulham Palace Road,
Hammersmith, London W6 8JB
1160 Battery Street,
San Francisco, California 94111-1213

First published by Thorsons 1994
1 3 5 7 9 10 8 6 4 2

A catalogue record for this book
is available from the British Library
ISBN 0 7225 3008 0

Typeset by Harper Phototypesetters Limited,
Northampton, England
Printed and bound in Great Britain by
HarperCollinsManufacturing Glasgow

For Stuart
One day they will find the answers.

AMANDA

ACKNOWLEDGEMENTS

My thanks to the Fresh Fruit and Vegetable Bureau and the British Turkey and British Poussin Information Services for providing a great many of the recipes in this book. I have analysed them, provided serving suggestions to balance them nutritionally and included notes where appropriate.

CONTENTS

Section One

ALL ABOUT ANTIOXIDANTS

WHAT ARE
ANTIOXIDANTS?

Every now and then, the world of nutrition comes up with a new subject for us to get our teeth into. If the 1980s was the decade of fibre, the 1990s must be dedicated to the so-called 'antioxidant vitamins'.

So just what are they? Well, vitamins generally can be explained as organic substances needed in small amounts to keep the body in working order. They have a huge array of functions, from helping to release energy to stopping our teeth falling out. They are needed all over the body and help keep our blood, bones, muscle, brain, hair, skin, nails and so on functioning properly.

The discovery of vitamins began around the start of this century, and scientists gradually uncovered the secrets of this molecular world which holds the key to good health. Take vitamin C, for example. By the nineteenth century all good seafaring captains knew that giving fruit and vegetables to their sailors prevented scurvy, although they hadn't a clue why. The 'anti-scurvy' substance in limes and other foods was finally extracted and isolated in 1932 at Cambridge, and christened Vitamin C. Research of equal importance was going on elsewhere. In 1890 a Dutch doctor working in Java realized that patients who were given white rice developed weak legs. If wholegrain rice was provided the problem disappeared. Eventually the substance in the rice husk responsible for such dramatic effects was isolated and called vitamin B1. Work continued and other vitamins followed, including, A, all the B group, D, E and K.

This first wave of vitamin discovery created great excitement, and governments soon came up with recommendations for the ideal daily vitamin intake. The basis for the figures was the amount needed to stop deficiency diseases – for example, enough vitamin D to stop rickets, enough B1 to avoid beriberi and enough folic acid to prevent a type of anaemia. Today we have entered the second wave of vitamin research. There is now growing evidence that we may benefit from having more than the previously recommended minimum of certain vitamins in order to prevent deficiency disease. It seems that larger amounts of these vitamins may promote optimal health and perhaps even stave off some of the diseases of middle and old age, not to mention putting the brakes on the ageing process itself.

The vitamins in question are C, E and the vitamin A precursor, beta-carotene. Whilst chemically they are very different substances, they share a common function. They all act as antioxidants.

ANTIOXIDANTS AND FREE RADICALS

The oxygen we breathe is transferred from the lungs into the blood and transported to every cell in the body. Once inside a cell, it helps turn digested food into energy to drive all our activities. During this process of oxidation, and during other naturally occurring reactions in the body, it is possible for substances called free radicals to be formed. Chemically, free radicals lack an electron and are therefore very unstable, so in an attempt to stabilize themselves they go charging off in search of an electron. They're not choosey and they have no manners; they literally grab an electron from the nearest source, which could be a cell wall or some material inside the cell. The unsuspecting donor is left damaged.

To deal with these chemical loose cannons, the body has a defence system – an army of antioxidants, which includes the antioxidant vitamins. An antioxidant can give the free radical the electron it needs with no detrimental consequences to itself.

However, problems arise when there aren't enough antioxidants present to combat the number of free radicals being formed. If antioxidant intake is too low, one of the defence systems is weakened and a free radical is able to carry out a commando-style attack on cells. This sparks a cascade of damage all around it, and cell walls and even the insides of cells, possibly including genetic material, can be damaged.

Then there's the other side of the equation. In the modern industrialized world we are daily exposed to pollutants that increase the production of free radicals in the body. Car exhaust fumes, cigarette smoke, ultraviolet light through a damaged ozone layer - the list goes on. The evidence suggests that we often experience a 'double whammy', with both these problems occurring together.

FREE RADICAL DAMAGE

According to the so-called Free Radical theory of disease, the damage caused by these reactive molecules could be extensive and even deadly. The evidence so far points to free radicals playing a role in the development of Britain's biggest killers, heart disease and lung cancer. In addition to these two disease Goliaths of our modern world, research suggests that free radicals may be involved in other illnesses associated with ageing, including ones as diverse as cataracts and Parkinson's disease.

Heart Disease

To some extent we've been brainwashed into assuming that cholesterol equals heart disease. Apart from being a very simplistic approach to a multi-causal problem, this completely ignores another vital piece of the nutritional jigsaw in the development of heart disease - the antioxidant hypothesis. This is, according to one American academic, 'one of the most exciting areas of research on the market.'

The traditional theory for heart disease goes like this: clogging up of the arteries (atherosclerosis) begins when injury (often just normal wear and tear) occurs to the inner coat of the arterial wall. This damaged site takes up cholesterol and fat, which is carried on a protein substance known as LDL. LDL cholesterol collects on the artery wall, eventually forming a fatty plaque called an atheroma. It's this atheroma that blocks the artery, stops blood flowing freely, and causes heart attacks and haemorrhages.

According to the antioxidant theory, it's only when the LDL has had an electron removed by free radical attack that it gets taken up into the artery wall. This means that if there are plenty of antioxidants around to deactivate the free radical, the LDL isn't damaged and no atheroma is formed. It's also thought that oxidized LDL can actually cause the initial damage to the artery wall which starts off the LDL infiltration.

Cancer

Although it is thought that antioxidants may help to prevent cancer, it is not absolutely certain how. Scientists have discovered quite a few possibilities through painstaking research. One theory is that antioxidants may help to stop mutations that are triggered by free radical attack. In laboratory studies it has been found that if mutations are started in bacterial systems, the addition of beta-carotene can decrease the number of mutants formed. In other words, adding beta-carotene has helped stop malignant changes brought about by free radicals. Stopping free radicals from attacking the genetic material in the cell, the DNA, is certainly a possible role. Vitamin C may help by stimulating interferon production and may be important in inhibiting tumour spread and micrometastases. Vitamin E's likely role in cancer prevention is based on its ability to prevent damage to cell walls.

ANTIOXIDANTS ON TRIAL

CANCER AND HEART DISEASE

If antioxidants were put on trial to find out whether they had a role in preventing cancer and heart disease, the defence would come armed with some impressive evidence. They'd start by calling 'Population Studies' to the dock.

Population Studies

Studies around the world have consistently shown that there is a higher incidence of cancer in regions where fewer vegetables and fruit are eaten. When Dr Gladys Block, of Berkeley University in the States, looked at forty-six studies on non–hormone-related cancer, she found that in thirty-three of them people with high intakes of vitamin C were significantly protected. Eight studies on cancer of the mouth, larynx or oesophagus have all found that an increase risk is associated with low intakes of vitamin C. Twelve studies looked at foods rather than single nutrients. In six of these, low fruit intake was associated with increased risk of cancer. Three of them in particular found an extremely low intake of fruit in populations with an extremely high incidence of these cancers.

Population studies on pancreatic cancer also reveal a protective role for vitamin C. One piece of research showed a twofold reduction of risk associated with high intakes. For stomach cancer the protective effect of vitamin C is two to threefold, and there's similar evidence for cervical cancer too. The bladder, colon and rectum may also be protected by significant vitamin C intake.

Dr Block also looked at evidence for the hormone-related cancers, which include breast, ovary, endometrium and prostate. The most convincing link with vitamin C is for breast cancer.

As for beta carotene, several studies initially suggested that high levels of vegetable and fruit consumption were associated with a reduced risk of lung cancer in particular and possibly other cancers too. Further studies established a strong link between lung cancer and beta-carotene. It seems that the carotenoids, a group of which beta-carotene is a member, are protective. Other work shows links between stomach, bladder and cervical cancer and beta-carotene although the evidence so far is less persuasive than for lung cancer.

Specific examples may help make all these generalizations clearer. In a study in Washington County, Maryland, USA, 26,000 volunteers gave blood samples. Of this group 436 went on to develop cancer at nine different sites. The nutrient levels in their blood were compared to those of 756 people of the same age and sex who were still healthy. Those who had developed lung cancer were found to have had significantly lower levels of beta-carotene in their blood at the start of the trials than those who had remained healthy. The same was true for vitamin E.

Research in Finland indicated a protective role for vitamin E too, when 766 cancer patients were compared to 1,419 people without cancer. The strongest links were found between vitamin E intake and stomach and intestinal cancers.

One of the best population studies on cardiovascular disease was carried out on European men to investigate the north-south gradient of heart disease in Europe. The researchers studied about 100 healthy men aged between forty and forty-nine, from three areas.

The first area had a high incidence of heart disease, with 410 to 414 deaths per 100,000 men between forty and fifty-nine every year. These were from Glasgow, Edinburgh and Aberdeen and North and Southwest Finland.

The second had a moderate incidence of heart disease – around 250 deaths per 100,000 men per year. These men were from East Germany and Tel Aviv.

The third group had what is considered to be a low rate of heart disease, where less than 130 men died per 100,000 per year. These men came from the foothills in the Swiss Alps, Toulouse and Catalonia.

It was found that in areas with a high risk of heart disease, men had low levels of vitamins C and E in their blood, and vice versa. In the case of vitamin E the evidence was particularly convincing.

Another study carried out in Scotland alone adds weight to the defence case. Scientists looked at the link between angina and low blood levels of vitamins C, E and beta-carotene. Six thousand men aged between thirty-five and fifty-four took part. Of 110 men who had angina and 394 who didn't, the results showed a very significant link between levels of these antioxidants and the risk of angina.

Intervention Evidence

In addition to population studies the defence council would want some meatier evidence, such as situations where people had actually been given supplements of antioxidants to see if they had any effect on reducing disease.

At the time of writing there are lots of research programmes underway doing just this. These trials take years to complete, and over the next ten years we should see results coming in. In the meantime there is some work available to us:

Chewing betel quids is to Keralan fishermen in India what smoking is in the West. While we pay for our habit with one of the highest rates of lung cancer in the world, the Keralan fishermen are prone to mouth cancer. In the 1980s a fascinating study investigated the frequency of mouth cancer (oral leucoplakia). The fishermen were allowed to keep chewing on their tobacco-filled quids and one group was given beta-carotene. The results showed that beta-carotene induced remission in 15 per cent of cases and caused a 98 per cent reduction in the incidence of precancerous cells.

In America, researchers at Harvard University enrolled 87,000 nurses on a health study. Those given at least 100iu (approximately 100mg) of vitamin E daily for two years developed heart disease in only half as many cases as those who did not take vitamin E supplements.

Another trial, also at Harvard, studied 22,000 physicians. One group was given 30mg of beta-carotene every other day, one group a dummy capsule, another aspirin, and another aspirin and beta-carotene. The trial is continuing but the intermediate results are interesting. They found that of the men with a history of cardiac disease, those taking beta-carotene suffered half as many heart attacks, strokes and deaths as those on the placebo. No heart attacks occurred among those on aspirin and beta-carotene. The team are now starting a similar trial on post-menopausal women, in which they will be given beta-carotene and vitamin E, alone and in combination.

Finally, results from a recently completed study in China add yet more fascinating evidence to the world melting pot of data. It took place in Linxian, in rural North Central China, between 1985 and 1991. This area was chosen because it has one of the highest stomach and oesophageal cancer death rates in the world. Participants were given doses of nutrients, and it was found that the combination of E, beta-carotene and selenium (a mineral antioxidant, unlikely to be deficient in Western diets), significantly lowered death rates from cancer. Cancer deaths decreased by 13 per cent and, overall, deaths decreased by 9 per cent.

OTHER DISEASES

The defence case for antioxidants is looking pretty good in terms of cancer and heart disease. Is there any other circumstantial evidence to be considered?

Recent work in Finland on senile cataracts should really be brought to the jury's attention. It was found that low blood levels of the antioxidants beta-carotene and vitamin E were risk factors in the development of senile cataracts.

In America, back in 1966, blood samples were taken from 1,419 people aged between forty-seven and eighty-three. Between then and 1977 it was found that people with low levels of vitamin E were twice as likely to need cataract surgery as those with high levels. People with low vitamin E and beta-carotene levels had over two and a half times the risk of developing cataracts. This investigation led one of the researchers to suggest that oxidation of the lens by free radicals may be part of the process leading to cataracts. An adequate supply of antioxidants could modify this. Further research has suggested that antioxidants may even reverse the degeneration of the eye once it has started.

Investigations into the possible role of free radicals in the development of both Parkinson's disease and rheumatoid arthritis are currently being considered.

AGEING

Since time immemorial, people have been trying to find the key to staying young longer. Some go to extraordinary lengths and keep the wheels of an ever-burgeoning industry well oiled in an attempt to preserve their looks. Could antioxidants ever replace the attraction of facelifts? It's unlikely, but nevertheless, the link between antioxidants and ageing is interesting.

There is no doubt that the ageing process is incredibly complex, but relatively simple processes such as longevity-determinant genes may exist which control the ageing rate. Experimental work points to free radicals having a role to play in this. In tests on tissues in the laboratory, scientists looked to see if antioxidants may in themselves be longevity-determinant genes. In some tests they found a positive relationship between specific antioxidants and the lifespan of mammals. The antioxidants involved included carotenoids and vitamin E. The result of these and further tests led the researchers to conclude that free radicals are implicated in the ageing process. The number of antioxidants an individual has could be important in determining how susceptible they are to age-related diseases.

SUMMING UP

So you've had some of the evidence presented. It's a snapshot look into years of work from all over the world. If the most eminent researchers in the field of antioxidants were sitting on the jury, the consensus for the verdict would be that the material is fascinating and exciting, and they would certainly call for continued research in this area. The unanimous decision would be to tell people to go away and start eating more foods rich in the antioxidant vitamins C, E and beta-carotene.

This is just what the National Cancer Institute in America, the World Health Organization and the British government have told us to do. The first two advise us to increase our regular consumption of fruits and vegetables to five portions (500g) per day. That may well be easier said than done. In Britain the average adult's intake is more likely to be around 200g on a good day. Having vegetables as side dishes day in, day out and eating the same old fruit can be boring, and probably doesn't make you feel much like keeping up regular intakes. This is where the recipes in this book are designed to help. They have been specially developed to help you increase your intake of antioxidant vitamins while enjoying an exciting and varied diet.

HOW MUCH IS ENOUGH?

Many health bodies agree: five portions of fruit and vegetables a day should increase our antioxidant levels enough to give us some protection against disease. Some scientists think levels of beta-carotene and vitamin E may need to be a little higher than you can regularly consume on a daily basis. Professor Anthony Diplock of Guy's Hospital in London, for example, has suggested it may be wise to have a vitamin E intake of 50–80mg a day and 15mg of beta-carotene a day.

When trying to get up to your five a day, remember that it doesn't include potatoes and that one portion is about 75g or 3 oz. This is two heaped tablespoons of peas or sweetcorn, two medium carrots, a tomato, about 8 Brussels sprouts, or a medium portion of courgettes, cabbage, cauliflower or spinach. For fruit, 75g is a small apple, banana, orange, peach, pear or nectarine, a large plum, a kiwi fruit or two slices of mango. Dried fruits count too. Apricots are quite a good source of beta-carotene and others, such as prunes, figs and dates, contain some vitamin E.

You can also drink juices to increase your antioxidant intake. Anything from the familiar orange and grapefruit to tomato, pineapple, mango or cranberry. If you have a juicer, fresh vegetable juices are a great way of getting your antioxidants, and they may prove especially useful for people who find munching their way through mounds of vegetables a problem.

Nuts and seeds are usually packed with vitamin E so try to eat these regularly too, and include oils such as sunflower, sesame and walnut in your diet. Remember they are high in calories, so don't go overboard if you're watching your weight.

Cereals and grains are also a good source of vitamin E. The germ is especially rich, so wholemeal bread, for example, is a valuable food.

All the recipes in this book list approximately how much vitamin C, E and beta-carotene they contain per serving. This allows you to work out your own intake and adjust it accordingly.

The tables below show the common sources of each antioxidant vitamin, and these are the foods you should aim to include in your diet on a regular basis. Remember, all foods have their own nutritional 'character', and by eating a wide variety each day, you will get a good spread of nutrients. Keeping in mind the five-a-day rule will certainly put you on the right track. This isn't as difficult as it may at first seem. For example, just eating half a grapefruit with your breakfast, some salad with your lunch, followed by fruit mid-afternoon and generous helpings of vegetables with your dinner will give you your five portions without dramatically changing the way you eat.

TOP 10 SOURCES OF VITAMIN C

Green pepper (½)	96mg
Strawberries (100g)	87mg
Orange (1)	65mg
Grapefruit juice (200ml)	62mg
Kiwi fruit (1)	30mg
Cabbage (90g)	20mg
Peas (100g)	12mg
Potatoes (100g)	9mg
Tomato juice (200ml)	8mg
Fresh parsley (1 tbsp)	6mg

TOP 10 SOURCES OF BETA-CAROTENE

Sweet potato (1 medium)	5mg
Carrot (1 large)	4mg
Spinach (90g)	3mg
Red pepper (½)	3mg
Mango (1 small)	3mg
Spring greens (90g)	2mg
Cabbage (90g)	1mg
Broccoli (90g)	1mg
Tomatoes (2)	1mg
Apricots (4)	1mg

TOP 10 SOURCES OF VITAMIN E

Wheatgerm oil (1 tbsp)	18mg
Sunflower seeds (25g)	10mg
Sunflower oil (1 tbsp)	6mg
Almonds (30g)	7mg
Peanuts(30g)	3mg
Avocado (1 small)	3mg
Spinach (90g)	2mg
Broccoli (90g)	1mg
Brussels sprouts (100g)	1mg
Sesame seeds (1 tbsp)	1mg

SUPPLEMENTS

There's no substitute for a well-balanced diet that contains a good variety of foods. Eating a wide range of foods not only adds to our enjoyment but also helps provide the whole spectrum of nutrients we need, including protein, fats, carbohydrates, vitamins and minerals. Sometimes, however, certain groups of people have special needs that might not be met by diet alone, and they can benefit from taking extra nutrients in the form of a supplement. Elderly people, for example, may need a boost of vitamin D; occasionally pregnant women need extra iron; and women trying to become pregnant are advised to take folic acid supplements. Below are some of the main categories of people with special needs who may benefit from a well-balanced antioxidant supplement.

The Elderly
Some elderly people may find it hard to eat lots of fruit and vegetables or to shop and cook on a regular basis. If this is the case, then a supplement may be useful to act as a top-up.

Inner-City Dwellers
People who are exposed to excessive free radical production through industrial and car pollution might like to consider taking supplements. The extra free radicals that can be produced as a result of living in inner-city areas could mean that a particularly high level of antioxidants is required.

Smokers
Smoking has been shown to lower blood levels of vitamin C and beta-carotene, and it is possible that normal levels of C, E and beta-carotene are inadequate to deal with the smoking-related increase in free radical production. This idea is backed up by some unpublished research whereby smokers were given supplements or vitamins C, E or beta-carotene. During supplementation, the amount of reactive oxidants that are known to spark off smoking-related tissue damage and possibly bronchial carcinoma decreased.

Parkinson's Disease Sufferers
Trials in New York showed that high dosages of vitamins E and C given to patients with early Parkinson's disease delayed the time

before they needed treatment with the Parkinson's drug levodopa by an average of two and a half years. The results of this initial study suggest that the progression of Parkinson's disease may be slowed down by doses of these antioxidants. A big clinical trial is now underway in North America to see whether these exciting findings can be confirmed.

It would seem reasonable that in all these cases, a modest supplement containing 100–150mg of vitamin C, 50–80mg of vitamin E and 15mg of beta-carotene may be beneficial and should not lead to any toxicity problems. Single supplements containing all the antioxidant vitamins are now widely available. Brands include Boots and Sanatogen; and for those who prefer to avoid animal products, VitaBrit Vital 3 is available in a gelatin-free capsule.

VITAMIN VALUES: STORAGE, PREPARATION AND COOKING

VITAMIN C

Vitamin C is one of the most sensitive and easily destroyed vitamins, and needs to be treated with respect at all stages of the food chain, from harvest to final preparation. It is found in all citrus fruits, such as oranges, satsumas and grapefruit, and also in kiwi fruit, berries such as blackberries and strawberries, and certain vegetables too. All green leafy vegetables, such as dark cabbage and spinach, have good amounts of vitamin C. The vegetable with the highest amount is the green pepper. Parsley is also rich in vitamin C, while tomatoes, onions and potatoes provide a reasonable supply. Since potatoes are a staple in the UK and we eat them in such large quantities, they are actually one of the most important sources of this vitamin. As well as having important antioxidant functions in the body, vitamin C is also needed to keep tissues in good condition, and it must be present for the body to be able to absorb the mineral iron.

As a rule of thumb, fruits and vegetables that come straight from the field have the highest levels of vitamin C. Sadly there aren't many people lucky enough to have access to such fresh produce. Vitamin C levels decrease as time in storage goes by, but buying from large supermarkets, markets and greengrocers with a high turnover of goods will ensure vitamin C is still reasonably high. Processed food isn't all bad! Take frozen peas, which are frozen and packed within about an hour of harvesting. If you store and cook them according to the instructions on the pack, they can contain more than 67mg of vitamin C per 100g, whereas peas that have been stored for four days then cooked contain only 57mg per 100g.

Canned fruit and vegetables are another matter entirely. Canning involves cooking the food at a high temperature for long periods of time, and this means virtually all the vitamin C is destroyed even before you start reheating the contents at home.

It's best to use fruit and vegetables as soon after purchase as possible to ensure minimum loss of vitamin C. If you do need to store them, do so in a cool part of the kitchen or in a larder. Salad vegetables are best kept in the fridge.

The key to keeping in the C is to handle with care and prepare as close to cooking or serving as possible. Once the cell structure of vegetables or fruit is disturbed by cutting, vitamin C is exposed to the air and levels start to fall. When preparing salad leaves it's best to tear them rather than cut them, since this causes least damage. Don't prepare vegetables then leave them sitting around in water; again you'll start to lose the C as it leaches out into the water. To help keep vitamins intact, don't peel fruit and vegetables unless it's absolutely necessary. If you don't need to cook the food, so much the better. Levels of vitamin C will remain much higher if no heat is applied.

Since vitamin C dissolves in water, try to use the smallest possible amount of water when boiling vegetables. As it's also destroyed by heat, cook for the minimum amount of time too. This may mean gradually learning to enjoy slightly crisper vegetables than you are used to. If there's any water left from cooking vegetables, try to use it in another part of the meal, for example to make gravy or a soup. If you can steam vegetables this will help preserve the vitamin C. Stir-frying briefly in a small amount of oil also helps to retain nutrients. Never add bicarbonate of soda to help greens keep their colour; it almost completely destroys vitamin C.

Microwaving is a useful way of preserving vitamin C. Tests have shown that microwaving rather than boiling saves twice as much vitamin C in parsnips, cauliflowers and broccoli.

BETA-CAROTENE

Beta-carotene is nowhere near as sensitive as vitamin C. It is found in dark green vegetables such as broccoli, spinach and dark cabbages, and also in red, yellow and orange fruits and vegetables such as mangoes, apricots, carrots and tomatoes. It is not destroyed by cooking; in fact heat can improve the chances of it being absorbed. Beta-carotene in canned carrots is better absorbed than from fresh ones.

Beta-carotene is best absorbed by the body when there is a small amount of fat in the meal, such as a little salad dressing on green leaves, or some gravy with a roast meal and vegetables.

VITAMIN E

Vitamin E is found in dark green vegetables and in avocado pears, but the best sources are nuts, seeds and some cereals. Oils from these foods are also rich in vitamin E, with wheatgerm oil the richest. Vitamin E isn't soluble in water so, unlike vitamin C, it is not leached out of vegetables during cooking.

Vitamin E levels remain quite stable in other foods such as nuts, seeds and sunflower oils, too. However, it's always best to use them up as soon as possible after purchase.

Section Two

THE RECIPES

Understanding what antioxidants are and the need to increase them in our everyday diet is one thing. Putting this into practice on a regular basis may not be quite so easy. So here's some help!

This section provides lots of tasty, easy-to-prepare recipes, all of which are rich in antioxidants. The amounts of vitamin C, beta-carotene and vitamin E per serving have been calculated for each dish. The calories have also been included, so you can pick and choose the kind of intake you feel happy with. Most of the recipes aim to provide a complete meal, and include drinks, side salads, breads etc. to help ensure that your nutrient intake is well balanced. Not only are the recipes high in antioxidants but they also stick to the established guidelines for healthy eating. This means that about 45-50 per cent of their calories come from carbohydrate, about 35 per cent from fat and 15 per cent from protein. In addition, they are low in saturated fats. These are the proportions of nutrients we should be aiming at for a healthy diet. In real terms, what these figures mean is that we should be getting most of our calories from carbohydrate foods such as potatoes, bread, pasta and rice. These should be in much larger proportions on our plates than the protein part of the meal, such as fish, poultry or meat. Fat intake should be kept down, so this means using only small amounts in cooking and avoiding foods rich in fats such as pastry, cakes and biscuits, fatty meats, and processed meat products such as pork pies.

Most of the recipes use fresh vegetables and fruit. Don't be afraid to use frozen alternatives if you're in a rush and haven't got fresh ones in. Sometimes tinned vegetables can be used too, for example, tomatoes, sweetcorn, or pulses such as chickpeas.

Some of the recipes use common vegetables in unusual and imaginative ways. Don't be afraid to give them a whirl. Baked parsnips and boiled swede will seem light years ago once you've tried them spiced and in soufflés. Treat the 'five-a-day' rule as a chance to extend your culinary repertoire, and as you try new and exciting ways of cooking fruits and vegetables you'll find you have increased your intake without even thinking about it.

BREAKFAST

Breakfast is a meal that gradually seems to be losing its importance. Gone are the days when we sat down to big plates of eggs and bacon. Now most of us make do with cereal and perhaps a piece of toast as we rush to start the day.

There's plenty of controversy over whether having breakfast helps you concentrate better and be more alert during the rest of the morning, but there's little doubt that if you are feeling full when you leave home there's less likelihood of succumbing to sugary snacks on the way to work or school and half way through the morning. Some research has shown that people who eat breakfast tend to have a better overall diet, which seems to back this point up.

It's easy to get into a rut with breakfast, having the same thing day in, day out. So here are some recipes to stimulate your imagination and taste buds and help you start the day with a good helping of antioxidants. None of them takes long to prepare, and all are tasty and filling. Some are variations on familiar themes, like Apple and Almond Muesli; others like Strawberries on Rye or Mango Shake are ones you may not have thought of trying at breakfast time. For people who really can't bear the idea of eating first thing in the morning, some of the recipes, such as Special Salmon Bagel, are portable and could be taken with you to eat later in the morning.

Porridge with Sunflower Seeds

Porridge makes a warming start to the day. Most people find a version they can enjoy, whether it's served with a little salt in true Scots style or pepped up with a few extras.

78MG VITAMIN C • OMG BETA–CAROTENE • 7MG VITAMIN E • 328 CALORIES

Serves 1

200ml semi-skimmed milk
75g porridge oats
1 tbsp honey-roasted sunflower seeds
glass of orange juice, freshly squeezed or from a carton, to serve

Pour the milk into a small saucepan, add the porridge oats and bring slowly to a boil. Simmer for a few minutes to thicken, stirring constantly, then pour into a bowl. Sprinkle with the sunflower seeds and serve with the orange juice.

Autumn Cinnamon Compote

This fruit compote makes good use of the wide range of
dried fruit now available.

20MG VITAMIN C • 0.6MG BETA–CAROTENE •
0.5MG VITAMIN E • 240 CALORIES

Serves 2

25g dried apricots
40g dried figs
20g dried apples
20g dried pears
20g dried peaches
orange juice
cinnamon stick
2 tbsp low-fat plain yogurt
4 tsp toasted sesame seeds

Soak the dried fruit in the orange juice with the cinnamon stick
overnight. Place in a saucepan, heat gently and simmer for 15 minutes. Serve hot, topped with the yogurt and sprinkled with the
sesame seeds.

Fruit Kebabs with Poppyseed Crispbreads

58MG VITAMIN C • OMG BETA–CAROTENE •
1MG VITAMIN E • 178 CALORIES

Serves 2

1 small banana
1 apple
1 orange
1 kiwi fruit
2 poppyseed crispbreads
1 tbsp low-fat cream cheese

Peel the fruit where necessary then chop it into neat cubes and thread it on to skewers. Serve accompanied by the crispbreads, spread with cream cheese.

Banana and Date Muffin

70MG VITAMIN C • 0MG BETA–CAROTENE •
1MG VITAMIN E • 406 CALORIES

Serves 1

1 wholemeal muffin
1 medium banana
1 tbsp chopped dates
2 tsp sesame seeds
glass of grapefruit juice, freshly squeezed or from a carton, to serve

Slice the muffin in half and toast it. Mash the banana with a fork and stir in the chopped dates and the sesame seeds. Spread this mixture over the muffin and serve with the grapefruit juice.

Mango Shake

A fruit shake makes a nutritious start to the day without having to sit down and eat. Mangoes are rich in beta–carotene, so are a particularly good fruit to use, but other fruits such as nectarines or peaches can be substituted if you like.

78MG VITAMIN C • 4MG BETA–CAROTENE •
2MG VITAMIN E • 313 CALORIES

Serves 1

1 medium-sized ripe mango, peeled, stoned and cubed
250ml semi-skimmed milk
150g low-fat plain yogurt
mint sprigs to garnish

Purée the mango in a blender with the milk and yogurt. Chill if time allows, then serve garnished with mint sprigs.

Strawberries on Rye

Rye bread has quite a strong flavour, which is complemented by the mild, creamy cheese. Vitamin C-rich fresh strawberries add texture.

**77MG VITAMIN C • OMG BETA-CAROTENE •
IMG VITAMIN E • 200 CALORIES**

Serves 1

*1 tbsp low-fat cream cheese
2 slices of rye bread
100g strawberries, sliced*

Spread the cream cheese on the rye bread then top with the strawberries. Eat accompanied by extra strawberries or save for a mid-morning snack.

Apple and Almond Muesli

Muesli can get a bit tedious, so try pepping it up by adding extra nuts and fresh fruit. This will boost both vitamins E and C.

43MG VITAMIN C • 0MG BETA–CAROTENE • 5MG VITAMIN E • 390 CALORIES

Serves 1

50g muesli
2 tsp toasted flaked almonds
1 apple, grated
1 kiwi fruit, peeled and chopped
150ml semi-skimmed milk

Mix the muesli with the toasted almonds. Top with the grated apple and the kiwi fruit then pour over the milk to serve.

Citrus Fruit Cup with Peanut Butter Crumpets

Peanut butter is a useful source of vitamin E and protein. Since it is also high in fat it is a good idea to have it instead of, rather than as well as, butter or margarine.

61MG VITAMIN C • 0MG BETA–CAROTENE • 1MG VITAMIN E • 300 CALORIES

∾

Serves 1

1 small grapefruit
1 small orange
2 crumpets
tbsp peanut butter

Peel and slice the grapefruit and orange then mix them together in a bowl. Chill before serving. Follow the fruit cup with the crumpets, toasted and spread with crunchy peanut butter.

Special Salmon Bagel

Bagels are now widely available in supermarkets and make a pleasant change from ordinary bread and rolls. Buy vegetable juice in a carton or, if you have a juicer, make your own at home.

18MG VITAMIN C • 7MG BETA–CAROTENE •
2MG VITAMIN E • 290 CALORIES

Serves 1

1 bagel
2 tbsp low-fat fromage frais
25g smoked salmon
juice of ½ lemon
glass of chilled vegetable juice, to serve

Cut the bagel in half and spread it with the fromage frais. Divide the smoked salmon between each bagel half and sprinkle with the lemon juice. Serve with the chilled vegetable juice.

Poached Eggs on Granary

This traditional breakfast can be made extra nutritious by using granary
bread and serving it with grilled tomatoes.

**84MG VITAMIN C • 1MG BETA–CAROTENE •
3MG VITAMIN E • 378 CALORIES**

Serves 1

2 slices of granary bread
1 egg
2 tomatoes
sunflower margarine
200ml glass of pink grapefruit juice, freshly squeezed or from a carton, to serve

Toast the bread and cut it into triangles. Poach the egg and grill the
tomatoes. Spread the toast lightly with sunflower margarine and top
with the egg and tomatoes. Serve with the grapefruit juice.

Crispy Bacon and Tomato Baguette

There's no need to give up bacon for breakfast, as long as you choose the leanest back cuts and grill it instead of frying.

**14MG VITAMIN C • 1MG BETA–CAROTENE •
1MG VITAMIN E • 419 CALORIES**

Serves 1

*2 rashers lean back bacon
large chunk of granary stick
2 tsp butter
1 large tomato, sliced*

Grill the bacon until crisp then dice it. Heat the bread in the oven and split it open lengthways. Spread one side with the butter, then make a sandwich with the grilled bacon and sliced tomato.

Bruschetta

This is a slightly unusual way of serving 'tomatoes on toast'.
Garlic at breakfast may not be everyone's first choice but
this recipe could convert you.

106MG VITAMIN C • IMG BETA–CAROTENE •
2MG VITAMIN E • 310 CALORIES

❧

Serves 2

1 small French stick
1 clove garlic, peeled and cut in half
2 beefsteak tomatoes, peeled, seeded and chopped
1 tbsp chopped fresh basil
salt and freshly ground black pepper to taste
1 tsp extra virgin olive oil
glass of orange juice each, to serve

Cut the French bread in half lengthways. Lightly toast the cut side
only then rub with the garlic.

Mix together the chopped tomatoes and basil and season with salt
and pepper. Spoon this mixture over the bread and sprinkle with the
olive oil. Bake in the oven at 220°C/425°F/Gas Mark 7 for a few
minutes until crisp then serve with the orange juice.

English Breakfast

Sometimes it's nice to serve up a traditional English breakfast.
Here's one which includes all the basics and still manages to
provide some antioxidants.

29MG VITAMIN C • I.2MG BETA–CAROTENE •
3MG VITAMIN E • 33I CALORIES

Serves 1

1 rasher of lean back bacon
1 low-fat sausage
1 tomato
2 large mushrooms
2 slices of bread, toasted
1 egg
glass of pink grapefruit juice, freshly squeezed or from a carton, to taste

Grill the bacon, sausage, tomato and mushrooms, and poach the egg.
Serve with the toast and a glass of pink grapefruit juice.

Breakfast Sausage and Beans

A filling, country-style breakfast that is surprisingly rich in all three antioxidants. The baked beans provide both protein and fibre.

70MG VITAMIN C • 2MG BETA–CAROTENE • 1MG VITAMIN E • 315 CALORIES

Serves 1

small can of baked beans
1 low-fat sausage
½ small red pepper
dash of Worcestershire sauce
wholemeal bap

Grill the sausage and the red pepper until the sausage is cooked and the pepper softened, then cut them into slices. Pour the baked beans into a pan, stir in the sausage and red pepper and heat through, adding Worcestershire sauce to taste. Slice the bap and toast it under the grill on one side only. Transfer to a plate and spoon over the sausage and beans.

Quick Kedgeree

Having kedgeree for breakfast is a filling way to start the day, and especially good at weekends when you have more time to prepare it.

81MG VITAMIN C • 0MG BETA-CAROTENE • 1MG VITAMIN E • 385 CALORIES

Serves 1

50g easy-cook rice
1 tbsp peas
75g smoked haddock
25g mushrooms
2 tbsp low-fat plain yogurt
1 tsp curry paste
salt and freshly ground black pepper to taste
large chunk of bread
glass of ruby-red orange juice, to serve

Cook the rice in boiling salted water until just tender, adding the peas for the last few minutes. Drain and set aside. Lightly poach the smoked haddock, then drain and flake it. Grill the mushrooms and chop them. Blend the yogurt with the curry paste.

Mix together the rice and peas, haddock, mushrooms and seasoning to taste then stir in the yogurt. Warm through in a low oven, then serve with the bread and the orange juice.

PACKED LUNCHES

Rather like with breakfast, there's a danger of getting into a rut with packed lunches, making up the same thing each morning because it's easy and, well, at least you know you like it. Here are some healthy ideas for packed lunches to shake you out of the routine. They aren't hard to make and are all simple to transport.

Brie and Bacon Bap

If you don't have time to make up the spicy tomato juice to drink with
this sandwich, just have a small carton of tomato juice.

**23MG VITAMIN C • 0.5MG BETA–CAROTENE •
2MG VITAMIN E • 477 CALORIES**

Serves 1

1 rasher lean back bacon
1 large bap
40g Brie
100g grapes
200ml tomato juice
Worcestershire sauce
Tabasco sauce
lemon juice
salt and freshly ground black pepper to taste

Grill the bacon until crisp then dice it finely. Cut the bap in half,
spread it with the Brie and sprinkle with the bacon. Slice a few grapes,
add to the bacon, then cover with the other half of the bap. Serve
with the tomato juice spiked with Worcestershire sauce, Tabasco,
lemon juice and salt and pepper, and eat with the remaining grapes.

Crunchy Camembert Baguette

97MG VITAMIN C • 2MG BETA-CAROTENE •
1MG VITAMIN E • 508 CALORIES

Serves 1

100g baguette
40g Camembert
2 tsp cranberry sauce
shredded iceberg lettuce
½ papaya and ½ mango for dessert

Split the baguette down the middle and spread with the Camembert.
Add the cranberry sauce and plenty of iceberg lettuce. Peel and seed
the papaya, peel and stone the mango, then slice them both and mix
together to serve for dessert.

Chicken and Chicory Sandwich

53MG VITAMIN C • 0MG BETA–CAROTENE •
1MG VITAMIN E • 690 CALORIES

Serves 1

1 tsp sesame seeds
1 tbsp low-fat plain yogurt
salt and freshly ground black pepper to taste
2 slices granary bread, lightly buttered
60g cooked chicken, chopped
chicory leaves
packet of low-fat crisps
1 nectarine, for dessert

Mix together the sesame seeds, yogurt and salt and pepper then stir in
the chopped chicken. Spread this mixture over one slice of bread and
cover with chicory leaves, then top with the remaining slice of bread.
Have packet of low-fat crisps and a nectarine to follow the sandwich.

Carrot Soup

This soup can be made at home and taken to work in a Thermos flask, unless you're lucky enough to have a microwave to heat it through.

79MG VITAMIN C • 7MG BETA–CAROTENE •
2MG VITAMIN E • 321 CALORIES

Serves 1

1 tsp oil
2 carrots, chopped
1 small leek, trimmed and finely chopped
250–300ml vegetable stock
salt and freshly ground black pepper to taste
handful of chopped fresh coriander or parsley
wholemeal cheese scone, to serve

Heat the oil in a small pan, add the carrots and leek and cook gently for a few minutes. Pour in the stock, season and bring to the boil, then reduce the heat, cover and simmer for 15-20 minutes. Add the coriander or parsley, transfer the mixture to a blender or food processor and purée. Return the soup to the pan to heat through and serve with the wholemeal cheese scone.

Spinach and Red Pepper Omelette

This is a flat omelette rather than the classic French folded omelette, and is particularly good eaten cold.

174MG VITAMIN C • 7MG BETA–CAROTENE •
4MG VITAMIN E • 542 CALORIES

Serves 1

½ red pepper
90g fresh spinach
1 clove garlic, crushed (optional)
1 tsp olive oil
chopped fresh parsley
salt and freshly ground black pepper to taste
2 eggs
2 tbsp milk
1 slice of multigrain bread

For dessert
1 kiwi fruit, peeled and sliced
small bunch of green grapes
1 Granny Smith apple, cored and chopped
squeeze of lemon juice

Cut the red pepper half into 2 and place the pieces under a preheated grill. Cook until the skin is charred and blistered in places, then leave to cool slightly. Peel off the skin and cut the red pepper into strips.

Heat the olive oil in a small frying pan then saute the spinach, and the garlic if using, for a few minutes until wilted. Mix in the red pepper strips, parsley and seasoning. Lightly beat together the eggs and milk then pour this mixture over the vegetables and cook over a gentle heat until the omelette is set and lightly browned underneath. Place the omelette under a hot grill for a few minutes to finish cooking the top then turn out on to a plate. Serve cold, cut into wedges, and accompanied by the bread. Finish lunch with a green fruit salad made by mixing together the kiwi fruit, grapes, apple and a squeeze of lemon juice.

Avocado Dip with Rice Cakes

I4MG VITAMIN C • 5MG BETA–CAROTENE •
3MG VITAMIN E • 490 CALORIES

Serves 1

1 small avocado
1 tbsp lemon juice
hot pepper sauce, such as Tabasco
salt and freshly ground black pepper to taste
2 carrots
3 rice cakes
5 no-need-to-soak dried apricots, or fresh apricots, for dessert

Peel and stone the avocado then mash the flesh with the lemon juice, hot pepper sauce and seasoning. Peel the carrots and cut them into batons. Serve the avocado dip with the carrots and rice cakes, and have the apricots for dessert.

Sweet Potato Salad

97MG VITAMIN C • 5MG BETA–CAROTENE •
10MG VITAMIN E • 353 CALORIES ·

Serves 1

1 large sweet potato
1 egg, hard-boiled, shelled and chopped
1 tomato, chopped
2 tbsp mayonnaise
salt and freshly ground black pepper to taste
Chinese leaves
1 orange or other citrus fruit, for dessert

Cook the sweet potato in boiling salted water until tender then drain.
When cool enough to handle, peel and cut into chunks. Mix the
hard-boiled egg and the tomato with the mayonnaise, season well,
then stir in the potato chunks. Serve on a bed of Chinese leaves and
follow with an orange or other citrus fruit for dessert.

Greek Salad

18MG VITAMIN C • 0MG BETA–CAROTENE •
1MG VITAMIN E • 595 CALORIES

Serves 1

50g canned mixed beans, drained
40g feta cheese, cubed
1 tbsp vinaigrette dressing
chunk of sesame seed French stick
tinned or fresh pineapple chunks and 1 carton of low-fat plain yogurt, for dessert

Mix together the beans and feta cheese then stir in the vinaigrette.
Serve with the French stick and have the pineapple chunks and
yogurt to follow.

Salmon and Broccoli Lunch Box

64MG VITAMIN C • 0.5MG BETA-CAROTENE •
4MG VITAMIN E • 500 CALORIES

∾

Serves 1

50g coloured pasta bows
2 tsp lemon juice
60g low-fat fromage frais
1 tbsp chopped fresh flat-leaf parsley
salt and freshly ground black pepper to taste
50g broccoli florets, lightly steamed
50g canned salmon, drained and flaked
stewed blackberry and apple, for dessert

Cook the pasta bows in plenty of boiling salted water until *al dente* then drain and leave to cool. Mix the lemon juice with the fromage frais, parsley, salt and plenty of black pepper. Toss the pasta bows, broccoli and salmon into this mixture. Serve stewed blackberry and apple for dessert.

Sardine Rice Pot

**66MG VITAMIN C • OMG BETA–CAROTENE •
2MG VITAMIN E • 471 CALORIES**

Serves 1

50g cooked brown rice (un-cooked weight)
2 spring onions, chopped
1 tbsp chopped fresh basil
¼ green pepper, chopped
75g sardines canned in tomato sauce
2 tbsp reduced-fat mayonnaise
dash of Worcestershire sauce
1 large apple, for dessert

Mix together the rice, spring onions, basil, green pepper, sardines, mayonnaise and Worcestershire sauce. Serve followed by a large apple for dessert.

SOUPS, SALADS AND LIGHT MEALS

It's not always easy to find healthy, appetizing dishes that can be put together in a short space of time. The recipes in this chapter try to help overcome the problem. Some of the soups can be made up in larger quantities and used over several days or frozen. The salads, on the other hand, should be prepared just before eating so they are as fresh and vitamin packed as possible. For people who have a main meal at lunch time there are plenty of light recipes such as Chinese Spinach and Pine Nuts and Quick Courgette and Spinach Risotto; these also make satisfying supper dishes.

Hearty Vegetable Soup

This thick soup is not only packed with vitamins but it also contains protein from the kidney beans. Served with cheese scones, it makes a well-balanced complete meal.

47MG VITAMIN C • 3MG BETA–CAROTENE •
5MG VITAMIN E • 410 CALORIES

Serves 2

1 tbsp sunflower oil
½ onion, chopped
1 small leek, trimmed and sliced
1 potato, diced
1 carrot, diced
½ x 432g can kidney beans, drained
1 sprig of fresh thyme or ½ tsp dried thyme
600ml vegetable stock
2 tbsp chopped fresh parsley
salt and freshly ground black pepper to taste
2 cheese scones, to serve

Heat the oil in a large saucepan and sauté the onion and leek until softened. Add the potato and carrot and stir well, then add the kidney beans, thyme and stock and bring to the boil. Reduce the heat, cover and simmer for 25 minutes or until the vegetables are tender. Stir in the parsley and season to taste. Serve with warm cheese scones.

Celeriac and Almond Soup

Celeriac is gradually becoming more popular in this country. It adds a
special flavour to soups and casseroles.

26MG VITAMIN C • OMG BETA–CAROTENE •
3MG VITAMIN E • 480 CALORIES

Serves 4

50g flaked almonds
1 tbsp olive oil
1 small onion, chopped
1 medium celeriac, peeled and sliced
900ml vegetable or chicken stock
150ml low-fat plain yogurt
salt and freshly ground black pepper to taste
4 pitta breads, to serve

Toast the almonds under a grill for a few minutes until golden.
Reserve a few for garnish then put the rest into a blender or food
processor and work until finely ground. Set aside.

Heat the oil in a large saucepan, add the onion and cook gently
until softened. Add the celeriac and the stock, then bring to the boil,
cover and simmer for 30 minutes or until the celeriac is tender.
Transfer to a blender or food processor and purée until smooth.

Return the soup to the pan, stir in the yogurt and the ground
almonds and reheat gently. Season to taste, then serve the soup garnished with the reserved flaked almonds and accompanied by the
warmed pitta bread.

Bortsch

Bortsch provides a great opportunity to make use of an underrated
vegetable – beetroot.

I4MG VITAMIN C • 0MG BETA–CAROTENE •
I MG VITAMIN E • 248 CALORIES

Serves 4

1 onion, finely chopped
1 tbsp olive oil
3 cooked beetroot (without vinegar), peeled and chopped
1 clove garlic, crushed
600ml chicken or vegetable stock
salt and freshly ground black pepper to taste
8 slices of rye bread, to serve

Garnish
150ml soured cream
chopped fresh parsley and chives (optional)

Fry the onion gently in the olive oil until softened, making sure it
does not colour. Add the beetroot, garlic, stock and seasoning, bring
to the boil, then cover, reduce the heat and simmer gently for 5 minutes. Purée in a blender or food processor then leave to cool. Chill
the soup for at least 4 hours. Before serving, carefully stir in the
soured cream to achieve a marbled effect. Sprinkle with chopped
parsley and chives, if using, and serve with the rye bread.

Turkey and Sweetcorn Soup

This soup is particularly low in fat but is packed with protein
from the turkey.

**81MG VITAMIN C • IMG BETA-CAROTENE •
IMG VITAMIN E • 270 CALORIES**

Serves 4

1 litre turkey stock
1 small onion, finely chopped
1 small leek, trimmed and sliced
1 large potato, diced
150ml semi-skimmed milk
350g canned sweetcorn kernels
225g cooked turkey meat (no skin), diced
1 yellow pepper, chopped
1 tbsp chopped fresh parsley
chunk of sun-dried tomato bread or wholemeal bread, to serve

Pour the stock into a large pan and add the onion, leek and potato.
Bring to the boil then reduce the heat, cover and simmer for 30 minutes. Add the milk then transfer the mixture to a blender or food
processor and purée. Return the soup to the pan and stir in the
sweetcorn, turkey and yellow pepper. Cook gently for 10 minutes
to heat through then serve garnished with the parsley and accompanied by the bread.

Yellow Pepper and Carrot Soup

Peppers are one of the richest vegetable sources of Vitamin C and carrots one of the richest sources of beta-carotene, so this soup is bursting with goodness.

100MG VITAMIN C • 6MG BETA-CAROTENE •
2MG VITAMIN E • 254 CALORIES

Serves 2

2 yellow peppers, seeded and chopped
2 potatoes, chopped
4 carrots, chopped
salt and freshly ground black pepper to taste
2 granary rolls, to serve

Put 450ml water in a large pan, add the peppers, potatoes, carrots and seasoning and simmer for 20 minutes or until the vegetables are tender. Cool the soup slightly, then purée in a blender or food processor. Return to the pan and heat through. Taste and adjust the seasoning, then serve with the hot granary rolls.

Spinach and Nutmeg Soup

This soup has a wonderful nutty flavour which is enhanced by the nutmeg. It's a great way of including spinach in family meals if boiled spinach gets the thumbs-down.

61MG VITAMIN C • 8MG BETA-CAROTENE •
16MG VITAMIN E • 450 CALORIES

Serves 2

2 tsp sunflower oil
1 onion, finely chopped
450g fresh or frozen leaf spinach
½ tsp freshly grated nutmeg
75g ground almonds
450ml vegetable stock
salt and freshly ground black pepper to taste
2 poppyseed wholemeal rolls, to serve

Heat the oil in a pan then add the onion and cook for 3 minutes until softened. Add the spinach and cook until wilted. Stir in the nutmeg, ground almonds and vegetable stock then bring to the boil and simmer for 5 minutes. Cool slightly then transfer to a blender or food processor and purée. Return the soup to the pan and heat through. Serve with the poppyseed wholemeal rolls.

Parsnip and Apple Soup

Parsnips tend to be restricted to Sundays, when they are roasted with a joint of meat. This soup makes use of their thickening qualities and sweetish flavour.

**20MG VITAMIN C • 4MG BETA–CAROTENE •
2MG VITAMIN E • 400 CALORIES**

Serves 4

*1 tbsp olive oil
2 large parsnips, peeled and diced
1 onion, chopped
1 small potato, diced
2 eating apples, peeled, cored and diced
600ml vegetable stock
salt and freshly ground black pepper to taste
1 tbsp toasted flaked almonds
chunks of herb bread, to serve*

Heat the oil in a saucepan and gently fry the vegetables and apples for 5 minutes. Add the stock and bring to the boil, then reduce the heat and simmer covered, for 30 minutes. Remove from the heat, cool slightly, then transfer to a blender or food processor and purée. Return the soup to the pan to heat through, then season to taste. Serve garnished with the flaked almonds and accompanied by good chunks of herb bread.

Lettuce Vichyssoise

Lettuce isn't something you'd usually think of putting in a soup, but this recipe works well.

21MG VITAMIN C • 0.5MG BETA-CAROTENE •
2MG VITAMIN E • 210 CALORIES

❦

Serves 4

1 tbsp olive oil
225g leeks, trimmed and sliced
2 potatoes, chopped
1 clove garlic, crushed
2 large lettuces
900ml chicken or vegetable stock
salt and freshly ground black pepper to taste
3 tbsp thick plain yogurt
8 slices of rye bread, to serve

Heat the oil in a large saucepan and gently fry the leeks, potatoes and garlic in it for 5 minutes. Chop the lettuce and set aside some for garnish. Add the rest to the pan with the stock and salt and pepper. Bring to the boil then reduce the heat, cover and simmer gently until the vegetables are just tender. Cool slightly, then transfer the soup to a blender or food processor and purée until smooth. Leave to cool, then whisk the yogurt into the soup and chill for 3-4 hours. Stir in the reserved lettuce, finely shredded, and serve with the rye bread.

Crunchy Vegetables with Avocado Dip

Avocados are one of the few vegetables that contain oil, and it is this that gives them their silky texture, ideal for dips.

**84MG VITAMIN C • 2MG BETA–CAROTENE •
2MG VITAMIN E • 400 CALORIES**

Serves 2

*1 large ripe avocado
1 tbsp lemon juice
freshly ground black pepper
175g low-fat fromage frais
1 broccoli spear, cut into florets
4 cherry tomatoes
¼ each of a small red, yellow and green pepper, seeded and cut into strips
1 large carrot, cut into batons
½ cucumber, cut into chunks
1 large pitta bread, cut into strips*

To make the dip, peel and stone the avocado then mash it with the lemon juice and black pepper to taste. Stir in the fromage frais and serve immediately, with the vegetables and pitta strips arranged attractively on a plate.

Two-Tone Salad

22MG VITAMIN C • 0.5MG BETA–CAROTENE •
1MG VITAMIN E • 200 CALORIES

Serves 4

1 medium celeriac
juice of 1 ½ lemons
2 chicory spears
115g mangetout
115g fresh beansprouts
100g canned chickpeas, drained
2 eggs, hard-boiled
small pot of low-fat plain yogurt
1 tsp sugar
1 clove garlic, crushed
2 tbsp chopped fresh parsley
salt and freshly ground black pepper to taste
4 chunks of raisin and nut bread, to serve

Peel the celeriac and grate or shred it coarsely, then mix it immediately with the juice of 1 lemon to prevent it discolouring. Cut the chicory into rings. Mix the celeriac, chicory, mangetout, beansprouts and chickpeas together in a salad bowl.

To make the dressing, crumble or sieve the hard-boiled egg yolks and mix them with the yogurt, sugar, garlic, parsley, seasoning and the remaining lemon juice. Chop the egg whites quite finely and stir into the dressing. Spoon the dressing over the salad ingredients and toss together. Serve with the raisin and nut bread.

Mini Nicoise

**83MG VITAMIN C • IMG BETA–CAROTENE •
7MG VITAMIN E • 500 CALORIES**

❧

Serves 2

*lettuce leaves
1 potato, cooked and diced
1 small can tuna, drained and flaked
2 size-3 eggs, hard boiled, shelled and sliced
½ green pepper, seeded and cut into strips
2 tbsp green beans, lightly cooked
2 tomatoes, chopped
25g black olives
4 anchovy fillets (optional)
1 tbsp vinaigrette dressing
2 wholemeal rolls*

Make a bed of lettuce on 2 plates then arrange the potato, tuna, egg,
green pepper, beans and tomatoes over it. Top with the olives and
anchovy fillets, if using, and drizzle with a little vinaigrette.

Sprouts Salad with Rice and Pine Nuts

Brussels sprouts don't need to be served cooked. In this recipe they are
shredded to make a tasty salad.

I30MG VITAMIN C • IMG BETA–CAROTENE •
3MG VITAMIN E • 334 CALORIES

Serves 4

450g Brussels sprouts
2 medium carrots, grated
2 tbsp finely chopped onion
2 tbsp sultanas
vinaigrette dressing
30g pine nuts
240g brown rice

Wash the Brussels sprouts and trim the base of each one, then shred
coarsely. Mix with the carrots, onion and sultanas then stir in suffi-
cient vinaigrette to moisten. Cook the brown rice in boiling salted
water until just tender, drain and mix in the pine nuts. Serve topped
with the salad.

Tomato and Pasta Salad

32MG VITAMIN C • IMG BETA–CAROTENE • IMG VITAMIN E • 308 CALORIES

Serves 4

175g pasta shapes
175g cherry tomatoes, halved
175g tomatoes, skinned
2 young courgettes, thinly sliced
1 tbsp chopped fresh parsley
salt and freshly ground black pepper to taste
3 tbsp low-fat plain yogurt
1 tbsp reduced fat salad cream
ciabatta loaf, to serve

Bring a large pan of water to the boil, add a little salt and the pasta and cook for about 8 minutes or until *al dente*. Drain and rinse in cold water, then drain again. Put the pasta into a bowl with the cherry tomatoes. Quarter the other tomatoes and remove the seeds then cut each quarter in half and add to the salad with the courgettes and parsley. Season with salt and black pepper.

Mix the yogurt and salad cream together and stir into the pasta. Chill, then serve with the ciabatta bread.

Calabrese Platter

This low-calorie salad is more interesting than plain cottage cheese and
lettuce. It's packed with all the antioxidants, too.

107MG VITAMIN C • 1MG BETA–CAROTENE •
2MG VITAMIN E • 220 CALORIES

Serves 6

600g calabrese
1 bunch of spring onions
2 heads of chicory
100g large radishes
6 tomatoes
300g cottage cheese
low calorie dressing
chopped fresh parsley and chives, to garnish
mixed grain or wholemeal rolls, to serve

Cook the calabrese in boiling salted water until just tender. Drain
well and allow to cool. Thinly slice the calabrese lengthways and
arrange in a star pattern on a large round white plate with the florets
facing outwards. Trim the spring onions, cut them in half lengthways
and arrange them and the chicory leaves between the slices of calabrese. Thinly slice the radishes and arrange around the centre. Cut
the tomatoes in half and scoop out the seeds. Fill the tomatoes with
the cottage cheese and place in the centre of the plate. Pour a little
dressing over the whole salad and sprinkle with the chopped herbs.
Serve with the rolls.

Ceviche

Don't be alarmed at the prospect of eating raw fish – it's 'cooked' in the citrus juice. Make sure the fish you buy is absolutely fresh.

106MG VITAMIN C • 2MG BETA–CAROTENE •
2MG VITAMIN E • 260 CALORIES

Serves 4

500g firm white fish fillets, such as cod, lemon sole, halibut or monkfish
juice of 5 limes
1 tbsp olive oil
2 cloves garlic, crushed
2 celery sticks, thinly sliced
3 tomatoes, skinned, seeded and chopped
1 small fresh green chilli, seeded and finely chopped
½ tsp ground cumin
1 small red onion, finely chopped
1 red pepper, seeded and thinly sliced
fresh coriander leaves and lime wedges, to garnish
4 slices of wholemeal bread, to serve

Skin the fish fillets, cut them into thin slices or small chunks and place in a glass dish. Pour over the lime juice, cover and refrigerate for at least 8 hours and up to 24 hours.

Heat the oil in a frying pan, add the garlic and celery and cook until they just begin to turn pale golden. Remove from the heat and cool, then stir in the tomatoes, chilli, cumin, onion and pepper. Lift the fish from the marinade and add to this mixture, then transfer it to a dish and refrigerate for 1 hour.

Serve garnished with coriander leaves and lime wedges and accompanied by the bread.

Halibut and Melon Salad with Tarragon

92MG VITAMIN C • 1MG BETA–CAROTENE • 2MG VITAMIN E • 470 CALORIES

∾

Serves 4

500g cooked, boned halibut, or other firm white fish
juice of 4 lemons and 1 lime
1 clove garlic, crushed
1 tbsp chopped fresh tarragon
salt and freshly ground black pepper to taste
2 small Charentais melons
small spinach leaves, lamb's lettuce, or sorrel
grated lemon or lime rind
sprigs of fresh tarragon, to garnish
1 baguette, to serve

Cut the fish into 2.5cm cubes and put them into a shallow dish. Add the lemon and lime juices, garlic, chopped tarragon and salt and pepper. Stir the fish so that it is evenly coated, then cover and chill for 4 hours.

Halve the melons and discard the seeds then scoop out the flesh with a melon baller. Stir the melon balls into the marinated fish, then spoon on to plates lined with spinach, lettuce or sorrel leaves. Scatter grated lemon or lime rind over the top and garnish with sprigs of fresh tarragon. Heat the baguette and serve with the salad.

Smoked Haddock and Avocado Salad

A pretty dish which makes a main course for four or a starter for six.

5MG VITAMIN C • 0MG BETA–CAROTENE •
1MG VITAMIN E • 328 CALORIES

Serves 4

350g smoked haddock fillet
750ml fish stock (made from fish stock cubes)
salt and freshly ground black pepper to taste
3 tbsp reduced-fat mayonnaise
1 tbsp chopped fresh dill plus sprigs of dill to garnish
75g peeled prawns
75g lettuce shredded
1 avocado, peeled, stoned and chopped
8 slices of wholemeal bread, to serve

Poach the smoked haddock fillet in the fish stock with salt and pepper to taste until just tender. Leave to cool then drain the fish thoroughly. Flake the cooled fish and mix with the mayonnaise, dill and peeled prawns.

Arrange the lettuce and avocado in scallop shells or on individual plates, spoon the fish mixture into the centre and garnish with sprigs of dill. Toast the bread and serve immediately with the salad.

BLT Open Sandwich

Here is a way of transforming a normally 'unhealthy' sandwich into one that conforms to healthy eating guidelines. Make sure you use lean back bacon and reduced-calorie mayonnaise.

54MG VITAMIN C • IMG BETA-CAROTENE • IMG VITAMIN E • 312 CALORIES

∾

Serves 2

4 rashers lean smoked back bacon, fat removed
4 slices of French bread
2 tsp reduced-calorie mayonnaise
2 large tomatoes, sliced
1 little Gem lettuce, shredded
salt and freshly ground black pepper to taste

Grill the bacon and lightly toast the bread. Spread the mayonnaise on the toast, place the bacon on top then arrange the tomatoes and lettuce on top of that. Season well and serve.

Baked Sweet Potatoes with Stilton

Sweet potatoes are the best single source of all three antioxidant vitamins. The ones with orange-coloured flesh contain more beta-carotene than their paler counterparts. This recipe makes a change from ordinary jacket potatoes.

44MG VITAMIN C • 8MG BETA-CAROTENE • 9MG VITAMIN E • 316 CALORIES

Serves 4

4 large sweet potatoes
a little oil
salt and freshly ground black pepper to taste
115g Stilton cheese, grated or crumbled
150g low-fat fromage frais
50g iceberg lettuce, finely shredded
finely chopped fresh parsley, to garnish

Wipe the potatoes with a damp cloth, rub the skins with a little oil and then with a little salt. Prick each potato three or four times and bake in the oven at 200°C/400°F/ Gas Mark 6 for 1 hour or until tender. Split each potato in half lengthways, and scoop most of the flesh into a bowl; mash, and then mix in just over half the Stilton, all the fromage frais, lettuce, and salt and pepper to taste. Spoon the mixture back into each potato skin and sprinkle with the remaining Stilton. Return to the oven for a further 5-10 minutes until the cheese has melted and the filling is hot. Serve sprinkled with chopped parsley.

Seafood-Stuffed Mushrooms

**57MG VITAMIN C • 1MG BETA-CAROTENE •
1MG VITAMIN E • 389 CALORIES**

Serves 4

*12 large open mushrooms
15g butter
1 stick celery, finely chopped
4 tbsp finely chopped red pepper
1 tsp curry powder
125g cooked peeled prawns, chopped
200g canned pink salmon, drained and flaked
2 tbsp mayonnaise
125g low-fat soft cheese
salt and freshly ground black pepper to taste
8 slices of wholemeal bread, to serve*

Remove the stalks from the mushrooms and chop them finely, then
put them into a frying pan with the butter, celery and red pepper
and cook for a few minutes until softened. Stir in the curry powder.
Transfer the mixture to a bowl and mix in the rest of the ingredients, then spoon into the mushrooms' caps. Cook on a prepared
barbecue for 8–10 minutes or bake in the oven at 190°C/375°F/
Gas Mark 5 for 15–20 minutes. Toast the bread and serve with the
stuffed mushrooms.

Hot Salmon Pitta

14MG VITAMIN C • 1MG BETA–CAROTENE •
2MG VITAMIN E • 465 CALORIES

Serves 2

200g canned salmon, drained and flaked
2 tbsp mayonnaise
5cm piece of cucumber, diced
1 spring onion, sliced
salt and freshly ground black pepper to taste
2 wholemeal pitta breads
2 tomatoes, sliced

Mix together the salmon, mayonnaise, cucumber, spring onion and seasoning. Put the pitta breads under a hot grill for a couple of minutes to warm through, then split them and fill with the salmon mixture and sliced tomatoes.

Pizza Muffins

Muffins make a good base for quick pizzas.

58MG VITAMIN C • 2MG BETA–CAROTENE •
2MG VITAMIN E • 340 CALORIES

Serves 2

1 courgette, thinly sliced
2 plain muffins
1 tsp olive oil
1 garlic clove, crushed
2 tbsp tomato purée
½ red pepper, seeded and cut into strips
salt and freshly ground black pepper to taste
25g pitted black olives, halved
100g reduced-fat cheese, grated

Cook the sliced courgette in a little boiling water for 1–2 minutes then drain. Split the toast and muffins. Mix the olive oil and garlic together and brush over the toasted muffins. In a bowl, mix together the tomato purée, courgette and red pepper. Season well. Spoon on to the muffins, scatter with the olives and cheese and grill for about 3 minutes, until the cheese is melted and golden.

Tikka Turkey

I IMG VITAMIN C • 0.5MG BETA–CAROTENE •
2MG VITAMIN E • 492 CALORIES

Serves 4

400g diced turkey meat or 4x100g turkey breast fillets, skin removed
300ml low-fat plain yogurt
2 tsp turmeric
2 tsp ground cumin
1 tsp cayenne pepper
1 tbsp lemon juice
400g naan bread
chopped tomato and cucumber, to serve

Place the turkey in a shallow dish. Mix the yogurt with the spices and lemon juice and pour this mixture over the turkey. Leave to marinate for about 2 hours in the refrigerator, then transfer the turkey to a roasting tin and bake in the oven at 200°C/400°F/Gas Mark 6 for 30 minutes. Serve with naan bread and chopped tomato and cucumber.

Mixed Herb Omelette

54MG VITAMIN C • 1MG BETA–CAROTENE •
3MG VITAMIN E • 350 CALORIES

ର

Serves 1

1-2 tbsp chopped fresh mixed herbs, such as parsley, chives and tarragon
2 eggs
salt and freshly ground black pepper to taste
2 tsp sunflower oil
2 cherry tomatoes, halved
1 large tomato, quartered
crusty caraway seed bread, to serve

Put the herbs, eggs and seasoning together into a bowl and beat lightly until combined. Heat the oil in a small frying pan and pour in the egg mixture. Keep lifting the edges with a fork so the uncooked egg on top runs underneath, then when the centre is just set, turn the omelette out on to a plate. Mix the tomatoes together, season and serve with the omelette, along with a chunk of crusty caraway seed bread.

Apricot, Almond and Orange Rice Pot

72MG VITAMIN C • 1MG BETA–CAROTENE • 7MG VITAMIN E • 450 CALORIES

Serves 2

6 no-need-to-soak dried apricots, chopped
1 large orange, peeled and cut into segments
200g cooked brown rice (cooked weight)
50g almonds, roughly chopped
salt and freshly ground black pepper to taste
1 tbsp lemon juice
2 tsp chopped fresh parsley

Toss the apricots and orange segments together with the rice and almonds. Season to taste, then sprinkle with the lemon juice and parsley.

Chinese Spinach and Pine Nuts with Noodles

Noodles make a pleasant change from rice and are very quick to cook. Both plain and egg noodles are available from good supermarkets.

65MG VITAMIN C • 9MG BETA-CAROTENE • 6MG VITAMIN E • 230 CALORIES

❧

Serves 4

900g fresh young spinach
600g plain noodles
100g mushrooms, finely sliced
1 tbsp sesame oil
¼ tsp Chinese five-spice powder
1 tbsp light soy sauce
1 large tbsp pine nuts

Remove any tough stalks from the spinach and wash the leaves very thoroughly. Place in a large pan with just the water that clings to the leaves, then cover and cool gently until the leaves have wilted. Drain well, then arrange in a serving dish and keep hot.

Cook the noodles, according to the directions on the packet. Quickly saute the mushrooms in the oil until softened. Stir in the five-spice powder, soy sauce and pine nuts and stir-fry for 1 minute. Spoon over the spinach and serve immediately with the noodles.

Barbecued Seafood Kebabs

65MG VITAMIN C • 0MG BETA–CAROTENE •
1MG VITAMIN E • 407 CALORIES

Serves 4

5 limes
1 red chilli, chopped
1 tbsp oil, plus extra for brushing
salt and freshly ground black pepper to taste
8 large peeled prawns
700g firm white fish fillets such as monkfish or cod, skinned and cut into
2.5cm cubes
1 yellow pepper, seeded and chopped
240g brown rice

Grate the rind and squeeze the juice from 2 of the limes, and put into a dish with the chopped chilli, oil and salt and pepper. Add the prawns and white fish, toss to coat with the marinade, then cover and refrigerate for 1 hour.

Cut each remaining lime into 8 wedges and arrange on 8 skewers with the fish cubes, prawns and the yellow pepper. Cook the rice in plenty of boiling salted water until just tender then drain. Meanwhile, brush the kebabs with oil and cook on a prepared barbecue or under a medium–hot grill for 6-10 minutes, turning once and brushing with the marinade. Serve with the rice.

Vine Leaves Stuffed with Tuna and Courgettes

**31MG VITAMIN C • 1MG BETA–CAROTENE •
5MG VITAMIN E • 390 CALORIES**

❧

Serves 4

200g canned tuna fish, drained
2 eggs, hard-boiled, shelled and chopped
1 tbsp chopped fresh chives, plus a few whole chives to garnish
finely grated rind of ½ lemon
1 clove garlic, crushed
½ iceberg lettuce, finely shredded
2 courgettes, coarsely grated
2 tbsp fresh wholemeal breadcrumbs
salt and freshly ground black pepper to taste
16 vine leaves, rinsed
300ml fresh tomato sauce
1 tbsp capers
180g buckwheat
3 tbsp raisins

Mix the tuna fish with the eggs, chives, lemon rind, garlic, lettuce, courgettes, breadcrumbs and salt and pepper. Divide the mixture into 8 portions, mould each one into a sausage shape and wrap in 2 vine leaves, tucking in the ends. Place in a small pan, spoon over the tomato sauce and add the capers. Cover and simmer for 40 minutes.

Meanwhile, cook the buckwheat in boiling salted water for about 15 minutes or until tender, then drain thoroughly and stir in the raisins. Serve the vine leaves hot or cold, garnished with a small spray of fresh chives and accompanied by the buckwheat.

Stuffed Peppers with Honey-Roasted Sunflower Seeds

Honey-roasted sunflower seeds are irresistible. You can find them in health-food stores and some supermarkets. Like other seeds and nuts they are rich in vitamin E as well as providing protein. Combine this with all the vitamin C and beta-carotene from the peppers and carrots and this is one antioxidant-rich dish.

138MG VITAMIN C • 15MG BETA–CAROTENE •
6MG VITAMIN E • 373 CALORIES

Serves 4

700g carrots, chopped
about 250ml chicken or vegetable stock
1 large and 2 medium red peppers
salt and freshly ground black pepper to taste
75g shallots, finely chopped
1 tbsp olive oil
1 clove garlic, crushed
pinch of ground ginger, or to taste
1 egg yolk
3 tbsp Greek yogurt
finely chopped red pepper or ground paprika, to garnish
2 tbsp honey-roasted sunflower seeds
ciabatta bread, to serve

Cook the carrots in stock to cover until just tender then drain well. Grill the large red pepper under a high heat until the skin is blistered and charred. Cool slightly then peel off the skin. Cut the pepper in half and remove the seeds and membrane. Purée the carrots in a food processor or blender with the skinned red pepper and add salt and pepper to taste.

Fry the chopped shallots gently in the oil for 3 minutes, then add the garlic and cook for a further minute. Add the carrot and pepper purée and stir over a gentle heat until the excess moisture evaporates, then add the ground ginger. Blend the egg yolk with the Greek yogurt, then stir this mixture into the pan and heat gently, making sure it does not boil. Keep warm.

Halve the 2 medium peppers lengthwise and remove the seeds. Cook the pepper halves in boiling, salted water for 3–4 minutes then drain well and fill them with the pepper and carrot puree. Sprinkle over the chopped red pepper or paprika and the sunflower seeds and serve with chunks of hot ciabatta bread.

Quick Courgette and Spinach 'Risotto'

12MG VITAMIN C • 0.5MG BETA–CAROTENE •
1MG VITAMIN E • 290 CALORIES

Serves 4

240g brown rice
1 clove garlic, crushed
1 onion, chopped
1 tbsp olive oil
2 courgettes, cubed
90g fresh spinach
100g peas
salt and freshly ground black pepper to taste
green salad leaves, to serve

Cook the rice in plenty of boiling salted water until just tender then drain thoroughly. Meanwhile, fry the garlic and the onion in the olive oil until softened. Add the courgettes, spinach and peas and cook for 10 minutes, then season well. Stir the vegetable mixture into the rice and serve with green salad leaves.

MAIN MEALS

It's easy to serve a generous helping of vegetables with a favourite meat or fish dish to increase your vegetable intake, but it's also a good idea to have a repertoire of dishes in which vegetables play a starring role. The recipes in this chapter range from meat and fish to vegetarian dishes, and many of them are 'demi-veg' in character – meaning that the meat or fish element is balanced by a high vegetable content. By following both the recipes and serving suggestions, you will be sure to get a good supply of all nutrients, and not just the antioxidant vitamins.

Moroccan Spring Lamb

Lamb can be fatty, so it's best to trim off the visible fat. There'll still be some in the flesh to add flavour.

89MG VITAMIN C • 2MG BETA-CAROTENE •
1MG VITAMIN E • 500 CALORIES

Serves 2

250g lamb fillet, all visible fat removed, cut into large cubes
1 tsp ground cinnamon
2 onions, sliced
100g no-need-to-soak dried prunes, halved
300ml lamb or vegetable stock
200g boiled potatoes
spring greens

Heat a heavy-based pan, add the lamb and the cinnamon and fry for 1 minute. Stir in the onions, prunes and stock. Bring to the boil then cover, reduce the heat and simmer for about 30 minutes until the meat is tender. Serve with steamed spring greens and boiled potatoes.

Pork and Lentil Casserole

Pork can be almost as lean as chicken, and is just as versatile. In this simple casserole it is combined with carrots, one of the best sources of beta-carotene.

31MG VITAMIN C • 4MG BETA-CAROTENE •
IMG VITAMIN E • 500 CALORIES

Serves 4

4 large baking potatoes, to serve
250g carrots, cut into chunks
1 large courgette, cut into chunks
100g mushrooms, quartered
1 tbsp olive oil
500g lean boneless pork, cut into cubes
1 medium onion, sliced
salt and freshly ground black pepper to taste
50g brown lentils
450ml chicken stock
1 tsp cornflour

Put the potatoes into an oven preheated to 200°C/400°F/Gas Mark 6 and bake until tender. Heat the oil in a frying pan and fry the pork briskly until well browned. Transfer the meat to a large saucepan. Put the onion, carrots, courgette and mushrooms into the frying pan and fry for a few minutes, then add to the pan with the pork. Season with salt and pepper and add the lentils.

Pour the chicken stock into the frying pan and bring to the boil. Pour the stock over the casserole, bring to the boil, then reduce the heat, cover and simmer for about 40 minutes until the meat is tender.

Mix the cornflour with a little cold water. Stir this mixture into the casserole and cook until thickened. Serve with the baked potatoes.

Beef and Lettuce Stroganoff

There's no need to ban red meat from a healthy diet, particularly as it's one of the best sources of iron. Just make sure it's a good lean cut. Most of the vitamin C in this dish comes from the parsley. Use it whenever you can, as it always helps boost levels of this vitamin.

12MG VITAMIN C • 0MG BETA–CAROTENE • 1MG VITAMIN E • 464 CALORIES

Serves 4

240g rice
1 medium onion, chopped
2 tbsp olive oil
450g beef fillet, cut into thin strips
½ iceberg lettuce, finely shredded
1 clove garlic, crushed
100g button mushrooms, sliced
salt and freshly ground black pepper to taste
4 tbsp dry sherry
150ml low-fat plain yogurt
a good handful of parsley, chopped

Cook the rice in plenty of boiling salted water until just tender then drain. Meanwhile, fry the onion gently in the olive oil in a large shallow pan for 3 minutes. Add the strips of beef and cook, stirring, until the meat is sealed on the outside. Add the lettuce, garlic, mushrooms, salt and pepper and the sherry. Simmer for 3-4 minutes then stir in the yogurt. Sprinkle over the parsley, then serve the stroganoff with the rice.

Chicken Breasts with Raspberries

Fruit with meat isn't as unusual as it might seem: think of roast pork with apple sauce, or gammon and pineapple, for example. The combination of chicken and raspberries is extremely good.

17MG VITAMIN C • 1MG BETA-CAROTENE •
1MG VITAMIN E • 380 CALORIES

Serves 4

600g potatoes, to serve
4 skinned, boned chicken breasts (120g each)
2 tbsp plain flour
1 tbsp olive oil
4 tbsp raspberry vinegar
2 tbsp redcurrant jelly
4 tbsp port
salt and white pepper
100g fresh raspberries

Peel the potatoes and cook them in boiling salted water until tender, then drain and mash. Meanwhile, toss the chicken breasts in the flour then heat the oil in a pan and fry the chicken for about 4 minutes per side, until golden brown. Remove the chicken from the pan and keep warm. Deglaze the pan juices with the raspberry vinegar then add the redcurrant jelly and the port. Stir together and boil rapidly until the sauce thickens. Season to taste. Just before serving, add the fresh raspberries to the sauce. Pour the sauce over the chicken and serve with the mashed potatoes.

Barbecued Walnut Chicken Breasts

Most nuts are rich in vitamin C, and walnuts are no exception. This dish contains both walnuts and walnut oil to boost vitamin E levels, plus plenty of vitamin C from the peaches or nectarines.

53MG VITAMIN C • OMG BETA-CAROTENE • 13MG VITAMIN E • 700 CALORIES

Serves 4

4 skinned, boned chicken breasts (120g each)
3 tbsp walnut oil
juice of 1 lemon
2 cloves garlic, finely chopped
2 tbsp chopped fresh tarragon
1 tsp grated orange rind
salt and freshly ground black pepper to taste
50g walnuts, roughly chopped
2 tbsp medium dry sherry
280g brown rice
½ lettuce, roughly chopped
2 fresh peaches or nectarines, halved, stoned and sliced
sprigs of fresh tarragon, to garnish

Put the chicken breasts into a shallow dish and spike each one three or four times at regular intervals with the tip of a sharp knife (this allows the marinade to permeate the chicken). Mix half the walnut oil with the lemon juice, garlic, chopped tarragon, orange rind, salt and pepper, half the chopped walnuts and the sherry. Spoon this marinade evenly over the chicken then cover and chill for at least 4 hours, preferably overnight.

Lift the chicken breasts out of their marinade and thread each one on to a kebab skewer, lengthways. Cook over a moderately hot barbecue for 8-10 minutes, turning the chicken breasts once. Meanwhile, put the marinade into a small pan and allow it to bubble briskly on one side of the barbecue then add the remaining walnut oil and leave the pan over the barbecue to keep hot.

Cook the rice in plenty of boiling salted water until it is just tender, then drain. Toss the lettuce with the peach or nectarine slices and arrange on a shallow serving dish, then arrange the spiked chicken breasts on top. Spoon over the hot sauce and garnish with sprigs of tarragon and the remaining chopped walnuts.

Note: Alternatively, you can cook the marinated chicken breasts under a preheated grill for about 6 minutes on each side.

Chicken in Fruit and Calvados Sauce

Chicken is accompanied here by not just one fruit but three.

29MG VITAMIN C • 0.5MG BETA-CAROTENE • 2MG VITAMIN E • 513 CALORIES

Serves 6

6 skinned chicken breasts (120g each)
3 tbsp seasoned flour
25g butter
2 tbsp olive oil
1 medium onion, chopped
1 tsp ground coriander
¼ tsp ground cinnamon
¾ tsp powdered saffron
450ml chicken stock
450g Golden Delicious apples, cored and sliced
225g plums, halved and stoned
225g greengages, halved and stoned, (or 450g plums)
3 tbsp Calvados
900g boiled new potatoes, to serve
juice of ½ lemon
chopped fresh parsley, to garnish

Coat the chicken in the flour. Heat the butter and oil in a deep frying pan, add the onion and fry for 3-4 minutes, then add the chicken and fry until sealed. Add the spices and stir in the chicken stock, then cover and simmer for 20 minutes. Stir in all the fruit and the Calvados and simmer for 15-20 minutes, until the chicken is tender. Meanwhile, cook the new potatoes. Stir the lemon juice into the chicken mixture, sprinkle with chopped parsley and serve immediately with the potatoes.

Spiced Chicken with Kumquats

Kumquats are quite widely available these days and can usually be found in large supermarkets during the winter.

24MG VITAMIN C • IMG BETA–CAROTENE • IMG VITAMIN E • 764 CALORIES

∾

Serves 4

2 tbsp oil
1.5kg chicken, skinned and cut into 8 pieces
1 clove garlic, crushed
1 tsp ground cinnamon
1 tsp ground ginger
1 tsp ground coriander
grated rind and juice of 1 orange
240ml chicken stock
175g kumquats, halved
salt and freshly ground black pepper to taste
240g rice
fresh coriander leaves, to garnish

Heat the oil in a large frying pan, add the chicken pieces and cook over a medium heat for 2-3 minutes on each side until lightly browned. Transfer the chicken to an ovenproof casserole.

Pour off most of the oil from the pan then add the garlic and cook for 1 minute. Stir in the spices then add the orange rind and juice and the stock. Bring to the boil then pour over the chicken, add the kumquats and season to taste. Cook in the oven at 180°C/350°F/Gas Mark 4 for 45 minutes or until the chicken is tender. Meanwhile, cook the rice until just tender, then drain. Serve the chicken with the rice and garnished with fresh coriander leaves.

Honeyed Chicken Salad

48MG VITAMIN C • 0.5MG BETA–CAROTENE •
1MG VITAMIN C • 400 CALORIES

Serves 4

4 skinned, boned chicken breasts (120g each)
2 sprigs of parsley
a few celery leaves
salt and freshly ground black pepper to taste
2 tbsp olive oil
1 tbsp clear honey
4 tbsp orange juice
1 tsp coriander seeds, lightly crushed
1 large head of chicory, sliced
2 handfuls of curly endive
2 oranges, peeled and segmented
3 tbsp plain yogurt
1 small red onion, thinly sliced into rings
400g loaf of granary bread, to serve

To cook the chicken breasts, either place them in a frying pan with the parsley, celery leaves and seasoning, add 600ml water and poach for 10 minutes, or place each breast on a piece of foil, add the parsley, celery leaves and seasoning, then wrap them up and steam for 10–12 minutes. Put the cooked chicken breasts to one side to cool.

Mix together the oil, honey, orange juice and coriander seeds to make a marinade. Slice the chicken breasts and place in a shallow dish then pour over the marinade, cover and refrigerate for at least 2 hours.

Arrange the chicory and endive on serving plates, then add the chicken and orange segments. Mix the marinade with the yogurt and spoon over the salad. Garnish with the onion and serve with the granary bread.

Chicken, Potato and Herb Hotpot

A tasty hotpot packed with filling potatoes, plenty of garlic and onions to keep away colds, and some spinach for both colour and vitamin C.

23MG VITAMIN C • IMG BETA–CAROTENE •
IMG VITAMIN E • 390 CALORIES

❧

Serves 4

1 medium onion, finely chopped
1 clove garlic, crushed
1 tbsp olive oil
600g boned chicken, cut into 2.5cm cubes
25g wholemeal flour
600ml chicken stock
salt and freshly ground black pepper to taste
300g potatoes, peeled and cut into 1cm cubes
150g fresh spinach, finely shredded
1 tsp chopped fresh thyme
1 tbsp chopped fresh parsley

Gently fry the onion and garlic in the oil for 3 minutes. Add the cubed chicken and fry for 3-4 minutes, until sealed on both sides. Stir in the flour and cook for 30 seconds then gradually stir in the stock and bring to the boil. Simmer for 15 minutes. Add seasoning to taste and the cubed potatoes then simmer for a further 8-10 minutes. Add the spinach, thyme and parsley and simmer for a further 3 minutes or until all the ingredients are tender.

Chicken Liver Sauté

In this recipe, quickly cooked chicken livers are served on a bed of
potatoes and cabbage. Although potatoes are not especially high in
vitamin C, they make a useful contribution because we eat them in such
large quantities.

86MG VITAMIN C • 1MG BETA–CAROTENE •
1MG VITAMIN E • 355 CALORIES

Serves 2

350g potatoes
salt and freshly ground black pepper to taste
1 spring onion, finely chopped
175g Savoy cabbage, shredded
1 tbsp olive oil
225g chicken livers
½ tbsp brandy
1 tbsp chopped fresh parsley

Cook the potatoes in boiling salted water until tender then drain,
mash well, and season to taste. Blanch the spring onion and cabbage
in boiling water then drain well and mix with the potato. Heat the
oil in a pan and add the potato mixture. Cook for 15 minutes until
brown and crispy.

Meanwhile, preheat the grill, then toss the chicken livers in the
brandy and leave to marinate for 5 minutes. Grill the chicken livers
for 10 minutes, turning as necessary. Serve on a bed of the fried
potato mixture, sprinkled with parsley.

Poussin Grilled with Lime and Coriander

A simple marinade flavours and protects the poussin from the heat of the grill. Lemon or orange can be substituted for the lime, or you can use dry cider or white wine. This dish is perfect for summer barbecues.

22MG VITAMIN C • 6MG BETA-CAROTENE •
2MG VITAMIN E • 673 CALORIES

Serves 2

grated rind and juice of 2 limes
grated rind of 1 lemon
2 tbsp olive oil
4 shallots or 1 small onion, very finely chopped
1 tbsp chopped fresh coriander
salt and freshly ground black pepper to taste
2 spatchcocked poussins
300g carrots, sliced
120g basmati rice
fresh coriander leaves, to garnish

Preheat the grill to medium. Mix the grated lime and lemon rind with the lime juice and olive oil, then stir in the shallots or onion, chopped coriander and black pepper. Slash the poussins' breasts and legs at 2.5cm intervals and rub the marinade all over the birds. Cover and leave to marinate, turning occasionally, for 3-4 hours.

Place the birds, skin-side uppermost, 10cm from the grill and cook for 20-30 minutes, turning twice, until the skin is crisp and golden and the juices run clear when the meat is pierced at the thickest part. Meanwhile, cook the carrots in a little water until tender, then drain, purée and season to taste. Cook the basmati rice and serve with the poussins and the carrot purée. Garnish with coriander leaves.

Mediterranean Turkey Casserole

Turkey is full of protein and low in fat – it's a pity we don't use it more in day-to-day cooking. This turkey casserole makes a change from roasts, curries and sandwiches and can be made at any time of year, not just with the Christmas leftovers.

46MG VITAMIN C • 0.5MG BETA–CAROTENE •
2MG VITAMIN E • 431 CALORIES

Serves 4

4 large baking potatoes, to serve
2 tbsp olive oil
450g turkey, diced
1 onion, sliced
1 clove garlic, crushed
100g button mushrooms, quartered
225g courgettes, diced
280ml stock
400g canned chopped tomatoes
½ tsp dried basil
salt and freshly ground black pepper to taste

Put the potatoes into an oven preheated to 200°C/400°F/Gas Mark 6 and bake until tender. Meanwhile, heat the olive oil in a large pan and sauté the turkey and onion for 7-8 minutes. Add the garlic, mushrooms and courgettes and cook for 2 minutes. Pour in the stock and the tomatoes and season with the basil and salt and pepper. Cover and simmer for 20 minutes until the turkey is tender. Serve with the baked potatoes.

Turkey and Mango Salad

35MG VITAMIN C • 1MG BETA–CAROTENE •
1MG VITAMIN E • 536 CALORIES

❧

Serves 4

450g cooked turkey, thickly sliced then cut into long strips
1 medium mango, peeled, stoned and diced
4 tbsp mayonnaise
4 tbsp Greek yogurt
2 tbsp chopped fresh chives
pinch of cayenne pepper
2 small heads of chicory or 1 head of radicchio, shredded
1 bunch of watercress, trimmed and divided into sprigs
2 tbsp sesame seeds, to garnish (optional)
1 French stick, to serve

Put the turkey and mango into a bowl. Mix together the mayonnaise, Greek yogurt, chives and cayenne pepper and fold into the turkey mixture.

Arrange the chicory or radicchio and the watercress on 4 individual plates then spoon the turkey mixture into the centre. If using the sesame seeds, toast them in a hot frying pan, shaking until the seeds are golden. Leave to cool then scatter over the turkey. Heat the bread and serve with the salad.

Pasta with Grilled Duck and Roasted Peppers

When you add peppers to a dish you can be sure it will be rich in vitamin C as well as some beta–carotene. In this recipe the oriental flavours in the dressing make a pleasant change.

148MG VITAMIN C • 5MG BETA–CAROTENE •
1MG VITAMIN E • 507 CALORIES

Serves 2

1 red pepper halved
½ yellow pepper
½ orange pepper
2 duck breasts
200g spaghetti or fettuccine

For the dressing
1cm piece of root ginger, peeled and grated
½ bunch of spring onions, finely sliced
2 tbsp soy sauce
2 tbsp lemon juice
2 tsp white wine vinegar
1 tbsp clear honey

Grill the peppers until their skins become charred. Put them in a plastic bag and leave for 10 minutes. Whisk together the dressing ingredients.
   Grill the duck breasts for 10 minutes per side. Cook the pasta until *al dente*, then drain. Skin the peppers and cut them into strips. Remove the fat from the duck breasts ; slice the duck and mix with the peppers. Pour over the dressing and serve with the pasta.

Stir-fried Duck and Mangetout with Pomegranate

Duck can be fatty but if you remove the skin and visible fat this is greatly reduced. A lot of the fat is the monounsaturated type, which is an important part of a healthy diet.

39MG VITAMIN C • 4MG BETA–CAROTENE •
1MG VITAMIN E • 402 CALORIES

Serves 4

4 duck breasts (150g each), skin and fat removed
¼ tsp ground ginger
2 shallots, finely chopped
2 cloves garlic, crushed
2 tsp coriander seeds, finely crushed
juice of ½ lemon
240g rice
2 tbsp oil
250g mangetout, topped, tailed and cut into strips
200g carrots, cut into thin strips
90ml dry red wine
180ml chicken stock
salt and freshly ground black pepper to taste
1 tsp cornflour
½ pomegranate

Cut the duck breasts into thin strips and put them into a bowl with the ginger, shallots, garlic, coriander seeds and lemon juice. Cover and leave to marinate for 1 hour.

Cook the rice in plenty of boiling salted water until just tender then drain thoroughly. Meanwhile, heat the oil in a large frying pan or wok, add the duck and its marinade and stir-fry for 5 minutes. Add the mangetout and carrot strips and continue to cook for 2 minutes then pour in the wine and stock and simmer for 2 minutes. Season to taste.

Blend the cornflour with a little water, stir into the pan with the pomegranate kernels and heat until the sauce thickens. Serve with the rice.

Grilled Cod with Baked Pumpkin and Ginger

It's a shame to restrict pumpkin to sweet pies and Hallowe'en. They add an interesting flavour and texture to meals and, you've probably guessed, some beta-carotene, since they are such a vibrant orange colour.

81MG VITAMIN C • 2MG BETA–CAROTENE •
7MG VITAMIN E • 689 CALORIES

Serves 2

450g pumpkin, peeled, seeds removed, and cut into chunks
25g stem ginger and 150ml ginger syrup from the jar
2 oranges
salt and freshly ground black pepper to taste
1 tbsp sunflower oil
2 cod fillets, about 175g each
grated rind of ½ lemon
150ml white wine
pinch of paprika
200g wholewheat pasta, to serve

Boil the pumpkin for 7 minutes, drain and place in an ovenproof dish. Finely chop the ginger and sprinkle over the pumpkin. Grate the rind from the oranges, then remove all the peel and divide the oranges into segments. Sprinkle the rind over the pumpkin, together with the seasoning, oil and ginger syrup. Bake at 200°C/400°F/Gas Mark 6 for 35-40 minutes.

Meanwhile place the fish it in a bowl with the lemon rind, wine, paprika and seasoning and leave to marinate while the pumpkin is baking, then grill for about 8 minutes either side. Cook the pasta until *al dente* then drain. Serve the fish with the pumpkin, garnished with the orange segments, and accompanied by the pasta.

Trout with Pink Grapefruit and Courgettes

41MG VITAMIN C • 0.5MG BETA–CAROTENE • 1MG VITAMIN E • 645 CALORIES

&

Serves 4

2 pink grapefruit
2 shallots, finely chopped
150ml dry white wine
8 trout fillets
2 tbsp chopped fresh dill, plus sprigs of dill to garnish
salt and freshly ground black pepper to taste
40g butter
200g quick-cooking couscous, to serve
1 clove garlic, crushed
350g courgettes, cut into fine strips
1 tsp cornflour

Grate the rind from one of the grapefruit and put it into a shallow dish with the shallots and the wine. Cut away the peel and pith from both grapefruit then cut out the segments from between the membranes, holding the grapefruit over the dish so the juice drips in. Place the segments in a separate dish and set aside. Stir the wine and grapefruit juice together, then add the trout fillets, cover and leave to marinate for 30 minutes. Reserve 8 grapefruit segments and roughly chop the rest.

Remove the fillets from the marinade, place on a board, skin side down, and scatter over the dill. Season with salt and pepper then divide the chopped grapefruit between the fillets. Roll up each fillet and put in an ovenproof dish, then pour over the marinade and dot with half the butter. Cover and bake in the oven at 190°C/ 375°F/Gas Mark 5 for 15 minutes. Meanwhile, put the couscous in a bowl and pour over boiling water to cover by about 3cm. Cover the bowl and leave for 10 minutes, until all the water has been absorbed. Fluff up with a fork before serving.

Heat the rest of the butter in a frying pan, add the garlic and cook for 1 minute. Add the courgettes and cook gently for 3 minutes until only just tender. Arrange on a serving dish with the trout and reserved grapefruit segments and place the dish in a low oven to keep warm.

Strain the cooking juices from the trout into a saucepan and simmer for 2 minutes. Blend the cornflour with 1 tablespoon of water, add to the pan and cook until thickened, adding seasoning if necessary. Pour a little of the sauce over the trout, garnish with dill sprigs and serve with the couscous. Hand the remaining sauce separately.

Warm Seafood Salad

This warm salad makes a delicious and luxurious main course.

9MG VITAMIN C • 0.2MG BETA-CAROTENE • 2MG VITAMIN E • 388 CALORIES

Serves 4

selection of salad leaves, such as lollo rosso, radicchio, frise
2 tbsp olive oil
1 tbsp tarragon vinegar
2 tsp chopped fresh tarragon
salt and freshly ground black pepper to taste
250g asparagus
250g lemon sole fillets, skinned
6 tbsp dry white wine
125g peeled prawns
4 wholemeal bread rolls, to serve

Wash and dry the salad leaves and arrange them on 4 plates. Mix together the oil, vinegar, tarragon and seasoning to make a dressing and set aside. Trim the asparagus and cut it into 5cm lengths then steam it for 7 minutes, until tender. While the asparagus is cooking, cut the fish fillets in half lengthwise, then cut them across into thin strips. Place them in a frying pan with the wine and simmer until almost cooked, then add the prawns and cook for 2 minutes.

Lift the fish from the pan and divide it between the plates, then arrange the asparagus on the salad. Pour over the dressing and serve while the fish and asparagus are still warm. Serve with the wholemeal rolls.

New Potato and Smoked Mackerel Salad

Mackerel is a member of the oily fish family, which is rich in the fatty acids that help protect against heart disease. The potatoes and fresh citrus juices in this recipe complement its powerful flavour.

45MG VITAMIN C • 0MG BETA–CAROTENE •
IMG VITAMIN E • 565 CALORIES

∽

Serves 4

750g new potatoes
1 orange
2 tsp lemon juice
1 tbsp oil
225g smoked mackerel fillet, flaked
1 tsp chopped fresh thyme, plus sprigs of thyme to garnish
salt and freshly ground black pepper to taste
1 French stick, to serve, 100g per person

Cook the new potatoes in their skins in boiling salted water until tender, then drain and slice them. Grate the rind from the orange then remove all the peel and cut out the segments from between the membranes. Set the orange segments aside and mix the orange rind with the lemon juice and the oil in a large bowl. Stir in the potatoes while they are still warm, then stir in the orange segments, smoked mackerel and chopped thyme, together with salt and pepper to taste. Spoon the mixture into a shallow serving dish and border with sprigs of fresh thyme. Serve with the bread.

Caribbean Fish Stew

Packed with peppers, this dish is just bursting with vitamin C.

**128MG VITAMIN C • 2MG BETA–CAROTENE •
8MG VITAMIN E • 821 CALORIES**

Serves 4

250g unpeeled prawns
1 bay leaf
1 slice of lemon
2 cloves garlic, crushed
grated rind and juice of 1 lime
1 tsp chopped fresh ginger root
350g fresh tuna or swordfish, skinned and cubed
250g thick cod steak, skinned and cubed
320g brown rice
2 tbsp oil
1 small onion, finely chopped
1 red and 1 green pepper, seeded and diced
120ml dry white wine
1 tsp demerara sugar
1 small mango, peeled, stoned and diced
½ small pineapple, peeled, cored and chopped
salt and freshly ground black pepper to taste
2 tsp cornflour

Peel the prawns, put the shells into a saucepan, and refrigerate the prawns until needed. Add the bay leaf and lemon to the pan, cover the shells with water and bring to the boil. Simmer for 30 minutes. Meanwhile, put the garlic, lime rind and juice, and ginger into a dish, add the fish, toss together and marinate for 30 minutes. Cook the brown rice in plenty of boiling salted water until tender, then drain. Strain the prawn stock into a jug, return to a clean pan and boil until reduced to 150ml. Heat the oil in a large saucepan, add the onion and peppers and cook for 5 minutes over a medium heat. Add the reduced stock, the marinade (but not the fish) and the wine and sugar, and simmer for 15 minutes.

Stir in the cubes of fish and cook for 5 minutes then blend the cornflour with 1 tablespoon of water and stir it into the stew. Add the mango, pineapple and peeled prawns and cook for 3-4 minutes, until thickened. Taste, and season if necessary. Serve with the brown rice.

Spiced Plaice Salad

The plaice 'cooks' in the lemon juice, producing wonderfully firm but
tender results. However, you must use extremely fresh fish.

25MG VITAMIN C • OMG BETA-CAROTENE •
IMG VITAMIN E • 413 CALORIES

Serves 4

375g plaice fillets, skinned
2 tbsp soy sauce
2 tbsp olive oil
2 tsp wholegrain mustard
1 large clove garlic, crushed
2 red chillies, finely chopped
4 tbsp lemon juice
small piece of fresh ginger root, crushed
salt and freshly ground black pepper to taste
175g lettuce, finely shredded
3 spring onions, sliced on the diagonal
75g button mushrooms, thinly sliced
fresh coriander leaves to garnish
400g loaf of crusty granary bread, to serve

Cut the plaice fillets into long thin strips and place in a shallow dish.
Mix together the soy sauce, olive oil, mustard, garlic, chillies, lemon
juice, ginger and salt and pepper and spoon over the fish. Cover with
clingfilm and chill for 4 hours or overnight.

Mix the lettuce with the spring onions and mushrooms and
arrange in a border on 4 plates. Spoon the fish into the centre of the
salad. Trickle some of the marinade over the fish and salad and garnish with the coriander leaves. Serve with the granary bread.

Stuffed Red Mullet with Avocado Sauce

Lettuce doesn't have to be restricted to salads. In this dish it is used to stuff
the fish and to wrap them up and keep them moist.

26MG VITAMIN C • 0MG BETA–CAROTENE •
2MG VITAMIN E • 308 CALORIES

ℭℴ

Serves 6

6 medium red mullet, scaled, gutted and cleaned
salt and freshly ground black pepper to taste
1 iceberg lettuce
50g goat's cheese, crumbled
grated rind of ½ lemon
1 tsp pesto
200ml dry white wine
900g new potatoes, to serve
½ ripe avocado, peeled, stoned and roughly chopped
fresh basil leaves, to garnish

Season the mullet inside and out. Reserve 12 large iceberg lettuce
leaves then coarsely chop 115g lettuce and finely chop about 2 tablespoons. Mix the goat's cheese with the lemon rind, pesto, finely
chopped iceberg lettuce and salt and pepper to taste. Fill the cavity in
each red mullet with this mixture.

Blanch the reserved lettuce leaves in boiling water for 1 minute
and refresh immediately in cold water. Drain thoroughly. Wrap each
stuffed red mullet in 2 lettuce leaves and lay them side by side in an
ovenproof dish. Spoon the white wine over the fish and cover with
foil. Cook in the oven at 180°C/350°F/Gas Mark 4 for 30–35 minutes, until the mullet are just tender. Meanwhile, cook the potatoes
in boiling salted water until tender, then drain.

Lift the mullet on to a serving dish and keep warm. Put the cooking juices into a blender or food processor with the coarsely chopped lettuce and the chopped avocado and blend until smooth. Serve the mullet garnished with the basil and accompanied by the sauce and the new potatoes. (The sauce can be thinned with extra wine if liked.)

Vegetable and Seafood Pilaff

Never be afraid to use frozen peas. This recipe does. They have almost as much vitamin C as freshly picked ones, can be bought all year round and are a great convenience food. They're also rich in protein and fibre, as well as some of the B vitamins.

69MG VITAMIN C • 2MG BETA–CAROTENE • 3MG VITAMIN E • 428 CALORIES

Serves 4

4 tbsp olive oil
1 onion, chopped
175g brown rice
750ml chicken stock
salt and freshly ground black pepper to taste
2 tomatoes, diced
1 green or red pepper, deseeded, diced and blanched
100g frozen peas, cooked
100g peeled cooked prawns
300g fresh mussels in their shells, scraped and debearded
lemon wedges and chopped fresh parsley, to garnish

Heat the oil in a large frying pan and sauté the onion for 2 minutes, then add the rice and cook for 2–3 minutes longer. Add the stock and seasoning, bring to the boil then reduce the heat, cover and simmer for 35 minutes. Add all the remaining ingredients, setting aside a few prawns for garnish, cover and cook for a further 5–10 minutes. Garnish with the reserved prawns, lemon wedges and parsley.

Scallop and Courgette Kebabs

23MG VITAMIN C • 0.5MG BETA–CAROTENE •
IMG VITAMIN E • 415 CALORIES

Serves 4

280g scallops, cleaned and cut in half
2 tbsp olive oil
salt and freshly ground black pepper to taste
1 bay leaf
1 tsp freshly squeezed lemon or orange juice
2 medium courgettes, cut into 1cm slices
8 cherry tomatoes, left whole, or 2 large tomatoes, cut into quarters
8 button mushrooms
300g wholewheat or green tagliatelle, to serve
1-2 tbsp chopped fresh dill, fennel leaves or parsley, to garnish

Place the scallops in a dish. Mix together the oil, seasoning, bay leaf
and lemon or orange juice, pour this marinade over the scallops,
cover and chill for 1 hour. Thread a piece of scallop on to a kebab
skewer followed by a slice of courgette, a tomato and a mushroom.
Repeat with 3 more skewers.

Cook the tagliatelle in plenty of boiling salted water until *al dente*
then drain thoroughly. Meanwhile, grill the kebabs for about 6-8
minutes under a moderate heat, brushing them frequently with the
marinade. Serve hot, sprinkled with fennel, dill or parsley, on a bed
of tagliatelle with a green-leaf salad.

Grilled Sardines with Lemon

This is very quick and simple to prepare, particularly if you ask your fishmonger to gut the fish first. A tomato salad makes a good accompaniment instead of the grated carrots, if you prefer.

4MG VITAMIN C • 2MG BETA–CAROTENE •
1MG VITAMIN E • 492 CALORIES

Serves 4

8 large sardines (about 480g in total)
2-3 tsp olive oil
a little lemon juice
freshly ground black pepper to taste
2 lemons, cut into wedges
sprigs of fresh parsley
100g carrots, grated
2 tsp toasted sesame seeds
1 apple, chopped
crusty bread or couscous, to serve, 100g per person

Clean the sardines: slit them along the belly and remove the innards then wash them well under running water. Brush the fish with the olive oil and sprinkle with lemon juice and black pepper. Brush a very heavy-based frying pan with a little oil and set over a fierce heat. When the pan is piping hot, fry the fish briskly for 3–4 minutes on each side. Arrange on a warmed serving dish and decorate with lemon wedges and sprigs of parsley. Mix together the carrots, toasted sesame seeds and chopped apple and serve alongside the sardines, with hot crusty bread or couscous.

Mackerel with Fruit Pickle

**5 1MG VITAMIN C • OMG BETA–CAROTENE •
1MG VITAMIN E • 544 CALORIES**

Serves 4

*1 dessert apple, cored and finely chopped
1 kiwi fruit, peeled and cut into ½ cm pieces
5 kumquats, thinly sliced
6 strawberries, hulled and roughly chopped
3 tbsp cider vinegar
1 tbsp coarsegrain mustard
4 medium mackerel, scaled, cleaned and gutted
½ iceberg lettuce, coarsely shredded
1 medium onion, thinly sliced
150ml dry white wine or chicken stock
salt and freshly ground black pepper to taste*

To make the fruit pickle, mix the apple, kiwi fruit, kumquats and strawberries together, then stir in the cider vinegar mixed with the mustard. Fill the cavity of each mackerel with the fruit pickle; any leftover pickle can be served separately.

Place each mackerel on the shiny side of a rectangle of foil large enough to enclose the fish. Pull the edges of the foil up around the fish, scatter over the lettuce and onion then sprinkle with the wine or stock and season with salt and pepper. Pull the edges of the foil together to make a parcel, place on a baking sheet and bake in the oven at 190°C/375°F/Gas Mark 5 for 30–35 minutes or until the fish is tender. To test the fish, unwrap one of the parcels slightly and insert the point of a knife in the thickest part of the flesh. If the flesh flakes easily, it is done. Serve immediately, with a salad of your choice.

Sicilian Cauliflower

A tasty, simple way of serving cauliflower as a main meal, without coating it in a cheese sauce.

45MG VITAMIN C • IMG BETA–CAROTENE • IMG VITAMIN E • 400 CALORIES

ౚ

Serves 4

1 medium cauliflower
2 tbsp olive oil
1 large onion, chopped
12 black olives, pitted and sliced
6 anchovy fillets, chopped
salt and freshly ground black pepper to taste
½ tbsp chopped fresh rosemary
150ml red wine
4 wholemeal pitta breads, to serve

Divide the cauliflower into even-sized florets. Pour a little of the olive oil into a heavy non-stick pan. Add some of the onion, olives and anchovies. Add a layer of cauliflower, a sprinkling of oil and a very little salt. Repeat the layers until all the ingredients are used up. Finish by pouring over any remaining oil and the red wine. Cover and cook over a low heat until the cauliflower is tender. Do not mix up the ingredients by stirring. The liquid should have more or less evaporated by the time the cauliflower is cooked but, if necessary, raise the heat to boil it away. Turn it in to a warmed serving dish and serve with the hot wholemeal pitta breads.

Green and Yellow Noodles with Carrot and Dill Sauce

In this recipe the carrots are grated and tossed with the noodles, for a change.

10MG VITAMIN C • 1MG BETA–CAROTENE • OMG VITAMIN E • 640 CALORIES

Serves 4

230g green fettuccine
230g yellow tagliatelle
150ml thick plain yogurt
150ml low-fat mayonnaise
1 tbsp chopped fresh dill or 1 tsp dried dill
115g peeled cooked prawns
115g shelled and skinned young broad beans (or thawed frozen ones)
2 carrots, grated
salt and freshly ground black pepper to taste
freshly grated Parmesan cheese, to serve

Cook the pasta in boiling salted water for 8-10 minutes or until *al dente*. Meanwhile, put the yogurt, mayonnaise, dill, prawns and broad beans into the top of a double saucepan or in a basin placed over a pan of gently simmering water and heat through gently. Drain the cooked pasta thoroughly and toss with the grated carrots. Spoon into a warm bowl, add the sauce and toss together. Season to taste. Serve immediately with grated Parmesan cheese.

Potato and Leek Pie

114MG VITAMIN C • 3MG BETA–CAROTENE • 6MG VITAMIN E • 283 CALORIES

❧

Serves 4

3 large potatoes
2 leeks, trimmed and cut into rings
1 onion, thinly sliced
1 tbsp oil
100g curd cheese
2 tbsp chopped fresh chives
6 tomatoes, seeded and chopped
1 clove garlic, chopped
salt and freshly ground black pepper to taste
4 tbsp vegetable stock
2 tbsp freshly grated Parmesan cheese
450g purple broccoli, to serve

Boil the potatoes in their skins for 10 minutes then when they are cool enough to handle, peel and thinly slice them. Parboil the leeks for 1-2 minutes then drain thoroughly.

Fry the onion gently in the oil. Layer the onion, potato slices and leeks in an ovenproof dish with small knobs of curd cheese between each layer. Mix together the chives, tomatoes, garlic, salt and pepper and stock. Spoon this mixture over the potatoes, then sprinkle the Parmesan cheese on top. Bake in the oven at 190°C/375°F/Gas Mark 5 for 25 minutes or until tender. Meanwhile, cook the broccoli in a little water until just tender. Serve the pie hot, accompanied by the purple broccoli.

Vegetable Chilli

**60MG VITAMIN C • 1MG BETA–CAROTENE •
2MG VITAMIN E • 424 CALORIES**

Serves 4

1 tbsp vegetable oil
2 garlic cloves, crushed
1 onion, sliced
2 tsp chilli powder
2 large aubergines, halved and sliced
4 courgettes, sliced on the diagonal
400g can chopped tomatoes
salt and freshly ground black pepper to taste
175g button mushrooms, trimmed
1 fresh chilli, seeded and sliced (optional)
240g brown rice
400g can kidney beans, drained
3 tbsp chopped fresh parsley
25g Cheshire cheese, grated

Heat the oil, add the garlic and onion and cook gently for 3–4 minutes. Add the chilli powder and cook for 1 minute, then add the aubergines and cook for 2–3 minutes more. Add the courgettes, tomatoes and 300ml water. Season generously. Bring to the boil, then reduce the heat, cover and simmer for 15 minutes. Add the mushrooms and the fresh chilli, if using, and cook for a further 15 minutes. Meanwhile, cook the rice until just tender, then drain.

Add the kidney beans to the vegetable mixture, stir to mix thoroughly and simmer for 10 minutes. Serve garnished with the parsley and cheese and accompanied by the rice.

Vegetable Pizza

You can add your own favourite toppings to this. Try to avoid heavy peperoni and cheese and choose lots of fresh vegetables instead.

IOOMG VITAMIN C • 3MG BETA–CAROTENE • 4MG VITAMIN E • 450 CALORIES

Serves 4

450g strong white flour
1 tsp easyblend dried yeast
1 tsp salt
1 tbsp sunflower oil, plus extra for brushing
freshly ground black pepper to taste
400g spinach
1 red and 1 yellow pepper
425g can chopped tomatoes, drained
150g canned artichoke hearts, drained
2 tbsp capers

Mix the flour, yeast and salt together in a large bowl. Make a well in the centre and add 300ml tepid water and the oil. Mix thoroughly, then turn out on to a lightly floured surface and knead for about 10 minutes, until smooth and elastic (this can be done in a mixer with a dough hook). Roll out into 4 circles. Season with black pepper, brush over with a little sunflower oil and leave in a warm place for 20-30 minutes, until puffy. Meanwhile, steam the spinach until tender. Roast the peppers under a hot grill until charred and blistered, then peel off the skin, remove the seeds, and cut the peppers into strips.

Spread the tomatoes over the risen pizzas, then add the spinach, peppers, artichokes and capers. Season and bake in the oven at 230°C/425°F/Gas Mark 7 for about 20 minutes.

Tagliatelle with Spinach, Pine Nuts and Raisins

This is a tasty way of using spinach as a main course.

98MG VITAMIN C • 13MG BETA–CAROTENE • 12MG VITAMIN E • 494 CALORIES

Serves 4

1.5kg fresh young spinach
300g tagliatelle
2 tbsp olive oil
3 heaped tbsp pine nuts
1½ tbsp raisins
salt and freshly ground black pepper to taste
freshly grated nutmeg to taste

Rinse the spinach well and remove any tough stalks. Place in a large pan with just the water that is left on the leaves, cover and cook for a few minutes, tossing occasionally, until just wilted. Drain and squeeze out as much water as possible.

Cook the tagliatelle in plenty of boiling salted water until *al dente* then drain thoroughly. Meanwhile, heat the oil in a frying pan. Add the pine nuts and raisins and fry for a couple of minutes, then add the spinach and season with a little salt and plenty of black pepper and nutmeg. Toss over the heat until warmed through then serve immediately with the tagliatelle.

Spicy Chickpeas and Swede

You can use tinned chickpeas if more convenient. As they have already
been cooked, start the recipe by boiling the swede.

**22MG VITAMIN C • IMG BETA–CAROTENE •
3MG VITAMIN E • 400 CALORIES**

Serves 4

225g dried chickpeas, soaked overnight
225g swede, peeled and roughly chopped
salt and freshly ground black pepper to taste
25g butter
1 large onion, chopped
1 tsp cumin seeds
½ tsp dried oregano
pinch of paprika
1 level tbsp plain flour
5 medium tomatoes, skinned and chopped
50g reduced-fat Cheddar cheese, grated
4 wholemeal rolls, to serve

Drain the chickpeas and place them in a saucepan with cold water.
Bring to the boil, cover and simmer for 45 minutes. Drain well. Place
the swede in a saucepan, cover with salted water and boil. Simmer for
15-20 minutes. Drain and reserve 150ml of the cooking liquid.

Heat the butter in a saucepan and sauté the onion, cumin, oregano
and paprika for 1-2 minutes. Add the flour and cook, stirring, for 1-2
minutes, then add the reserved liquid and bring to the boil. Stir in the
tomatoes, cover and simmer for 2-3 minutes. Add the chickpeas and
swede and stir over a gentle heat until hot. Season and serve topped
with the cheese and accompanied by the rolls.

Egg Tatties

This recipe uses some favourite staples - potatoes, eggs and milk - to give a simple vegetable meal.

75MG VITAMIN C • 0MG BETA–CAROTENE •
2MG VITAMIN E • 390 CALORIES

Serves 2

2 large baking potatoes
3 eggs
1 tbsp semi-skimmed milk
salt and freshly ground black pepper to taste
1 tsp butter
1 tbsp chopped fresh chives
2 tbsp low-fat plain yogurt
crisp lettuce leaves and ½ green pepper, chopped, to serve

Wash the potatoes and prick the skins at regular intervals, then wrap them in foil and bake in the oven at 200°C/400°F/Gas Mark 6 for 1 ¼ hours, until tender.

Just before the potatoes are ready, beat the eggs with the milk and salt and pepper. Melt the butter in a small pan and stir in the eggs. Scramble lightly over a gentle heat until the eggs form soft creamy curds. Halve each potato lengthways and scoop out the flesh. Mash the potato flesh and mix lightly with the scrambled egg, chives and yogurt. Spoon back into the potato shells, cover loosely with foil and return to the oven for another 4–5 minutes. Serve with the lettuce and green pepper.

Parsnip and Carrot Souffle

Parsnips are a versatile root vegetable. Here is an unusual way of using
them - turning them into a soufflé.

I3MG VITAMIN C • 4MG BETA–CAROTENE •
2MG VITAMIN E • 432 CALORIES

Serves 4

4 medium parsnips, peeled and chopped
3 medium carrots, peeled and chopped
75g cream cheese
1 clove of garlic crushed
4 eggs, separated
salt and freshly ground black pepper to taste
French stick, to serve, 75g per person

Cook the parsnips and carrots in boiling salted water until tender.
Drain, then purée in a blender or food processor, or push through a
sieve. Beat in the cream cheese, garlic, egg yolks and salt and pepper
to taste.

Whisk the egg whites until stiff and fold into the purée. Pour into
a greased souffle dish and bake in the oven at 230°C/425°F/Gas
Mark 7 for about 20 minutes, until risen and golden. Serve at once,
with hot crusty French bread.

Celery and Tomato Gratin

Cooking celery opens up its potential uses. Here it is served with a tomato
sauce and Gruyère.

28MG VITAMIN C • IMG BETA-CAROTENE •
3MG VITAMIN E • 425 CALORIES

Serves 4

1 medium head of celery, cut into 5cm lengths
1 large onion, finely chopped
1 clove garlic, crushed
3 tbsp olive oil
450g tomatoes, skinned, seeded and chopped
½ tsp caster sugar
6 tbsp dry white wine or cider
salt and freshly ground black pepper to taste
16 pitted black olives
50g Gruyère cheese, grated
280g rice

Put the celery into a saucepan with enough water just to cover, and
bring to the boil. Simmer gently until just tender, then drain.
Meanwhile, gently fry the onion and garlic in the oil for 3-4 minutes.
Add the tomatoes, sugar, wine or cider, and salt and pepper to taste.
Simmer gently for 15 minutes.

Put the cooked celery into a greased ovenproof dish. Scatter the
olives over the top then pour over the tomato sauce and sprinkle with
the grated cheese. Bake in the oven at 200°C/400°F/Gas Mark 6 for
15 minutes. Cook the rice in plenty of boiling salted water until tender then drain and serve with the gratin.

Stuffed Aubergines

Aubergines are the ideal shape for stuffing.

60MG VITAMIN C • 1MG BETA-CAROTENE •
10MG VITAMIN E • 436 CALORIES

Serves 2

2 medium aubergines
2 tbsp sunflower oil
1 onion, chopped
225g cooked lentils (cooked weight)
3-4 tbsp chopped fresh parsley
½ tsp finely grated lemon rind
1 clove garlic, crushed
1 large tomato, chopped
175g cooked brown rice (cooked weight)
salt and freshly ground black pepper to taste
2 tbsp grated cheese
twists of lemon, to garnish

Cut the aubergines in half lengthways and scoop out the flesh to within 1cm of the skins. Chop the flesh. Blanch the aubergine shells in boiling water for 2 minutes then drain well.

Heat the oil and fry the aubergine flesh and the onion until soft. Add the lentils and cook for 3-4 minutes, then stir in all the remaining ingredients except the cheese and lemon twists. Stuff the aubergine shells with this mixture, cover and bake in the oven at 200°C/400°F/Gas Mark 6 for 15-20 minutes. Serve hot, garnished with a sprinkling of cheese and the lemon twists.

Stir-Fried Broccoli

You can get stuck in a rut with some stir-fry recipes. This one makes use of broccoli for a change.

47MG VITAMIN C • 0MG BETA-CAROTENE •
6MG VITAMIN E • 360 CALORIES

∾

Serves 4

240g rice
4 large broccoli stems
2 tbsp vegetable oil
salt to taste
½ tsp sugar
3 tbsp vegetable stock
1 tsp cornflour
3 spring onions, chopped
2 tbsp flaked almonds
2 tbsp honey-roasted sunflower seeds

Cook the rice in plenty of boiling salted water until just tender, then drain. Cut the broccoli florets from the stems and separate into clusters, then set aside. Finely slice the stems. Heat the oil in a wok or large frying pan then stir-fry the broccoli stalks for about 1 minute. Add the florets and stir-fry for a further minute. Sprinkle with salt to taste, sugar and 2 tbsp of the stock, stirring for a few seconds to blend, then cover and cook over a moderate heat for 2–3 minutes. In a small bowl, blend the remaining stock with the cornflour to form a smooth paste. Pour this mixture into the pan then add the spring onions and flaked almonds and stir for a few seconds until the broccoli is coated with a light, clear glaze. Mix the rice and the sunflower seeds together and serve at once with the stir-fry.

DESSERTS

Desserts are an ideal opportunity to eat more fruit, and while you may find that you are usually happy to finish the meal with just a piece of raw fruit there are times when it's nice to have something a little more elaborate. This chapter covers the whole range, from simple fruit salads and compotes to winter warmers such as baked apples. Recipes such as Exotic Fruit Terrine and Sweetheart Rhubarb and Orange Mousse take a little more effort to prepare but are perfect for entertaining. There's no need to feel guilty about enjoying dessert with these recipes, since they are all rich in antioxidant vitamins. Fruit provides mainly vitamin C, plus some beta-carotene, while nuts and seeds add vitamin E.

Rhubarb Soufflé Omelette

3 1MG VITAMIN C • 0MG BETA–CAROTENE •
5MG VITAMIN E • 347 CALORIES

Serves 1

2 sticks rhubarb, trimmed and chopped
finely grated zest and juice of ½ orange
1 tsp caster sugar
2 eggs, separated
1 tbsp milk
small knob of butter
½ tsp brown sugar
1 tbsp Greek yogurt
1 tbsp flaked almonds
icing sugar

Place the rhubarb, orange juice and caster sugar in a small pan and poach until the rhubarb is tender. Beat the egg yolks, milk and orange zest together. In a separate bowl, whisk the egg whites until stiff then carefully fold into the egg yolk mixture. Heat the butter in an omelette pan and pour in the soufflé mixture. Cook over a low heat until the base has set. Put the rhubarb, brown sugar and yogurt in the centre of the omelette and cook for a further minute, then fold in half to enclose the filling. Turn out on to a plate and serve sprinkled with the almonds and a little icing sugar.

Exotic Fruit Terrine

47MG VITAMIN C • 0.5MG BETA–CAROTENE • 0.5MG VITAMIN E • 200 CALORIES

Serves 8

juice of 2 oranges
8 tsp powdered gelatine
3 tbsp caster sugar
900ml sparkling white grape juice
250g strawberries
1 kiwi fruit, peeled and sliced
1 ripe but firm mango, peeled, stoned and sliced
1 starfruit, sliced and pips removed
sprigs of fresh mint (optional)

Put the orange juice into a small bowl, sprinkle over the gelatine and leave to soak. Place the bowl in a pan of hot water and stir until the gelatine has dissolved. Stir in the sugar until dissolved then leave to cool. Gradually whisk in the grape juice then strain the mixture into a jug and place in the refrigerator until beginning to thicken. Skim off any froth that comes to the surface.

Halve 8-10 of the smallest strawberries and set aside, then slice the rest. Rinse a large loaf tin with cold water then stand it in a dish of ice cubes. Pour a little of the thickened jelly over the base (it will set quickly). Arrange the kiwi fruit down the centre and the halved strawberries along each side. Spoon over a little more jelly, then a layer of sliced strawberries. Continue with layers of fruit and jelly until the tin is full, finishing with a layer of jelly. Refrigerate until set.

Dip the tin in a bowl of hot water, and gently pull the edge of the jelly away from the tin. Turn upside down onto a plate. Garnish with sprigs of mint, if using, and serve within 24 hours.

Ruby Red Orange and Fig Compote

There's nothing like a drop of liqueur to pep up fruity desserts, and orange-flavoured liqueurs such as the ones suggested here are the obvious partners for oranges.

60MG VITAMIN C • OMG BETA–CAROTENE • OMG VITAMIN E • 183 CALORIES

Serves 4

225g dried figs (loose, not in a block)
1 tbsp honey
4 ruby red oranges
4 tbsp Cointreau, Grand Marnier or Curacao (optional)
matchstick strips of orange rind, to garnish
4 tbsp fromage frais, to serve

Wash the figs under running water, then put them in a pan, add water to cover and leave to soak for about 3 hours. Stir in the honey and cook the figs gently in their soaking water until just soft. Do not over-cook. Lift the figs out with a slotted spoon. Boil the honey syrup over a high heat until reduced and thickened, pour it over the figs and leave to cool.

Shortly before serving, peel the oranges, removing all the pith, then slice them thinly with a very sharp knife. Arrange the orange slices in a serving dish with the figs and syrup and sprinkle with liqueur, if liked. Serve cold but not chilled, garnished with strips of orange rind and accompanied by the fromage frais.

Sweetheart Rhubarb and Orange Mousse

30MG VITAMIN C • 0MG BETA–CAROTENE • 0MG VITAMIN E • 137 CALORIES

Serves 6

250g early rhubarb, cut into 2.5cm lengths
juice and finely grated rind of 1 orange
40g soft brown sugar
230g curd cheese, or other low-fat soft cheese
180ml low-fat plain yogurt
2 egg yolks (optional)
pink food colouring (optional)
4 tsp powdered gelatine

Sauce
2 stems rhubarb, cut into 4cm lengths
190ml dry white wine or cider
sugar to taste
1 tsp cornflour
pink food colouring (optional)
2 oranges, peeled and segmented, to garnish

Place the rhubarb in a small pan with the orange juice and poach until just tender. Transfer to a blender or food processor, add the sugar, curd cheese, yogurt and egg yolks, if using, and blend until smooth. Add a few drops of pink food colouring to tint the mixture, if liked.

Put the gelatine into a small bowl with 4 tbsp water, stand it in a pan of hot water and stir until dissolved. Add to the rhubarb mixture. Pour into 6 greased individual heart-shaped moulds or a greased and lined small loaf tin. Chill until set, then unmould carefully. If set in a loaf tin, cut into slices to serve.

For the sauce, put the rhubarb in a small pan with the dry white wine or cider, add sugar to taste and cook gently until the rhubarb is just tender but still holds its shape. Remove the rhubarb with a slotted spoon, cut it into thin strips and set aside. In a small bowl blend the cornflour with 2 tbsp water and stir into the cooking juices; heat gently until lightly thickened. Return the strips of rhubarb to the pan and leave to cool. Tint with pink food colouring, if liked. Serve the mousses on individual plates with the sauce poured around and garnished with orange segments.

Pink and White Fruit Kebabs with Strawberry Sauce

147MG VITAMIN C • 0MG BETA–CAROTENE • 0MG VITAMIN E • 130 CALORIES

Serves 4

450g strawberries
350g lychees, peeled and stones removed
grated rind and juice of 1 small orange
3 tbsp sweet white wine
75g strawberry fromage frais
2 tbsp yogurt

Put three-quarters of the strawberries and all the lychees into a bowl, add the orange rind and juice and the wine and toss together. Cover and chill for 1 hour, then remove the fruit and thread it on to 8 small bamboo skewers.

To make the sauce, puree the remaining strawberries with the fromage frais then sieve into a bowl. Add 2 tbsp of the fruit marinade and whisk together until smooth.

To serve, pour a pool of strawberry sauce on to 4 serving plates. Add dots of yogurt and then use the tip of a knife to create a swirled effect. Place 2 kebabs on each plate and serve.

Autumn Puddings

This healthy, filling pudding uses apples and pears along with blackberries, which are a surprisingly good source of vitamin E.

25MG VITAMIN C • 0MG BETA–CAROTENE • 3MG VITAMIN E • 422 CALORIES

Serves 4

a little oil for brushing
8 thin slices of wholemeal bread, crusts removed
150ml apple juice
50g granulated sugar
juice of ½ lemon
2 eating apples, peeled, cored and sliced
1 pear, peeled, cored and sliced
75g blackberries
pinch of ground cinnamon
2 tsp powdered gelatine

Sauce
225g blackberries or blackcurrants
3 tbsp icing sugar
juice of ½ lemon

Garnish
thin slices of red-skinned apple
thin slices of ripe pear
juice of ½ lemon
sprigs of fresh mint

Brush the insides of 4 individual pudding basins with a little oil. Cut a circle of bread to fit the base of each pudding basin then cut the remaining bread into fingers and use to line the basins, trimming to fit where necessary.

Put the apple juice, sugar and lemon juice into a shallow pan and stir over a low heat until the sugar has dissolved. Add the apples and pear and poach gently for 4 minutes. Stir in the blackberries and leave to cool, then add cinnamon to taste.

Put the gelatine and 2 tbsp water into a small bowl, stand it in a pan of hot water and stir until the gelatine has dissolved. Add the gelatine to the cooled fruit mixture and chill until it is on the point of setting. Spoon it into the bread-lined pudding basins and chill until completely set.

To make the sauce, put the blackberries or blackcurrants into a pan with the icing sugar and lemon juice and simmer for 3 minutes. Pureé in a blender or food processor, then leave to cool. When ready to serve, carefully unmould each pudding on to a dessert plate and spoon the sauce over the top. Decorate with slices of apple and pear, brushed with lemon juice, and small sprigs of mint. Serve with yogurt, fromage frais, or a scoop of ice cream, if you like.

Summer Meringue Baskets

If you haven't got time to make meringue baskets for this recipe you can buy ready-made ones - only then you miss out on the vitamin E in the almonds.

**54MG VITAMIN C • 0MG BETA–CAROTENE •
3MG VITAMIN E • 382 CALORIES**

Serves 6

50g blanched almonds, lightly toasted
4 egg whites
250g caster sugar
125g raspberries
125g redcurrants
125g strawberries, hulled
1 kiwi fruit, peeled and diced
2 tbsp strawberry or raspberry liqueur (optional)

Line 2 baking sheets with non-stick paper and draw 6 oval shapes on the paper, then turn it over and place on a baking sheet. Finely chop the toasted almonds in a grinder or food processor. Put the egg whites into a bowl and beat with an electric whisk until stiff. Gradually add the caster sugar and continue to whisk until stiff and glossy. Fold in the almonds. Spread about one-third of the meringue over the oval shapes on the paper, then spoon the rest into a piping bag fitted with a nozzle and pipe round the edge of each oval.

Bake in the oven at 100°C/225°F/Gas Mark ¼ for about 2 hours until dry. Peel the paper off the meringues and cool on a wire rack. Put the fruit into a bowl and toss with the liqueur, if using, then divide between the meringue baskets. Serve immediately.

Grapefruit and Orange Blush

77MG VITAMIN C • 0MG BETA–CAROTENE •
0.5MG VITAMIN E • 90 CALORIES

Serves 4

1 pink and 1 yellow grapefruit
2 large oranges
4 tsp clear honey
4 tbsp Greek yogurt
¼ to ½ tsp ground cinnamon
4 sprigs of mint to garnish (optional)

Cut both grapefruit in half. With a sharp, stainless steel knife, carefully cut the segments away from the membrane and place in a bowl. Cut the membrane out of the grapefruit skins and discard, but reserve the skins. Grate the zest from ½ an orange and place in the bowl with the grapefruit. Remove the remaining peel and pith from both oranges and cut them into segments. Toss with the grapefruit, orange zest and honey then spoon this mixture into the grapefruit skins. Mix together the yogurt and cinnamon and top each grapefruit half with 1 tbsp of this mixture and a sprig of mint. Chill before serving.

Tropical Fruit Boats

Stuffed pineapple makes a lovely centrepiece in a buffet or a great dessert for a dinner party.

72MG VITAMIN C • IMG BETA–CAROTENE •
IMG VITAMIN E • 161 CALORIES

Serves 4
1 large pineapple
2 kiwi fruit, peeled and sliced
2 starfruit, sliced
1 mango, peeled, stoned and sliced
1 prickly pear, peeled and sliced
2 tbsp white rum
juice of ½ lemon

Cut the pineapple in half lengthways with a sharp knife so as to leave the top pine intact. Carefully scoop out the flesh, leaving a shell about 1cm thick. Cut the pineapple flesh into small cubes and place in a bowl with all the remaining fruit. Add the rum and lemon juice and toss well. Cover and chill for 1 hour then pile the fruit mixture and juices into the pineapple shells. To serve, scoop the fruit from the pineapple shells into small bowls.

Marmalade Baked Pears

I8MG VITAMIN C • OMG BETA–CAROTENE •
IMG VITAMIN E • I57 CALORIES

∾

Serves 4

4 firm pears
1 lemon, cut in half
6 tbsp reduced-sugar marmalade
2 cloves
4 tbsp cider
yogurt, to serve

Peel, halve and core the pears. Rub all over with the cut surface of a lemon half to prevent discolouration. Put the pears into a lightly greased ovenproof dish, rounded sides uppermost. Squeeze the juice from the lemon, put it in a small pan with the marmalade, cloves and cider and heat gently. Spoon the marmalade sauce evenly over the pears and bake in the oven at 180°C/350°F/Gas Mark 4 for 30–35 minutes, until tender. Serve either hot or cold, with yogurt.

Mango Yogurt Mousse

**64MG VITAMIN C • 3MG BETA-CAROTENE •
2MG VITAMIN E • 166 CALORIES**

Serves 4

*1 large mango, peeled, stoned and diced
300ml yogurt
2 tbsp golden granulated sugar
1 ½ tbsp powdered gelatine
3 tbsp orange juice
2 egg whites*

Purée the mango flesh in a blender or food processor with the yogurt and sugar until smooth. Put the gelatine and orange juice into a small bowl, stand it in a bowl of hot water and stir until dissolved, then stir it into the mango purée. Leave it in a cool place until it begins to thicken. Whisk the egg whites until stiff but not dry and fold lightly but thoroughly into the mango mixture. Spoon into 4 tall stemmed glasses and chill for about 3 hours before serving.

Baked Apples with Toasted Almonds

**22MG VITAMIN C • 0MG BETA–CAROTENE •
2MG VITAMIN E • 159 CALORIES**

Serves 4

*4 large cooking apples
3 tbsp raisins
2 tbsp chopped toasted almonds
grated rind of 1 lemon
3 tbsp water
4 tbsp low-fat plain yogurt*

Wash and core the apples. Chop a quarter off the bottom of each core and put it back into the apples to act as a stopper. Score round the circumference of each apple with a sharp knife and place them in an ovenproof dish.

Mix the raisins with 1 tbsp of the chopped almonds and the grated lemon rind and press this mixture firmly into the apples. Pour 3 tbsp water into the ovenproof dish and bake the apples in the oven at 180°C/350°F/Gas Mark 4 for 45 minutes–1 hour until they are soft all the way through. Serve each apple topped with a spoonful of yogurt and sprinkled with the remaining almonds.

Winter Fruit Salad

OMG VITAMIN C • OMG BETA–CAROTENE •
2MG VITAMIN E • 274 CALORIES

Serves 4

4 dried figs
8 prunes
8 dried apricots
4 dried peach halves
4 dried pear halves
4 dried apple rings
4 cloves
a little sugar or honey (optional)
4 tbsp low-fat fromage frais
1 tbsp honey-roasted sunflower seeds

Wash the fruit, put it in a pan with the cloves and soak overnight in 250ml water. Cook the fruit in the same water for about 20 minutes, until tender. Add a little sugar or honey to sweeten, if necessary, then serve hot or cold, topped with the fromage frais and sunflower seeds.

DRINKS

Drinks can be an easy and tasty way of boosting your antioxidant intake, ranging from a simple glass of fruit juice to the recipes provided here. Apricots, mangoes and carrots will boost beta-carotene levels while citrus-based drinks or ones with strawberries are full of vitamin C. If you're lucky enough to own a juicer then try experimenting with combinations of vegetables and fruits to create drinks that can go with anything, from breakfasts to packed lunches or as a between-meal filler.

Apricot Shake

32MG VITAMIN C • 0.5MG BETA–CAROTENE • 1MG VITAMIN E • 183 CALORIES

Serves 1

100g fresh apricots, stewed in a little water then cooled and stoned
100ml skimmed milk
150ml low-fat plain yogurt
100ml mango juice
sprig of mint, to garnish

Blend together all the ingredients except the mint in a blender or food processor. Serve chilled, with plenty of ice cubes and a sprig of mint for decoration.

Carrot and Coriander Cocktail

**27MG VITAMIN C • 14MG BETA-CAROTENE •
1MG VITAMIN E • 52 CALORIES**

Serves 1

*200ml carrot juice
handful of chopped fresh coriander leaves
1 tbsp lime juice
freshly ground black pepper to taste*

Blend all the ingredients together in a blender or food processor, reserving a little coriander for garnish. This drink really needs to be well chilled before serving.

Spicy Virgin Mary

21MG VITAMIN C • 0.5MG BETA–CAROTENE • 2MG VITAMIN E • 52 CALORIES

Serves 1

200ml tomato juice
dash of Worcestershire sauce
dash of Tabasco sauce
2 tsp lemon juice
freshly ground black pepper to taste
pinch of celery salt
1 celery stick

Place all the ingredients except the celery stick in a cocktail shaker or container with a tight-fitting lid and shake well. Taste and adjust the seasoning. Serve with plenty of ice and the celery stick in the glass.

Strawberry and Almond Crush

80MG VITAMIN C • 0MG BETA–CAROTENE •
3MG VITAMIN E • 180 CALORIES

Serves 1

100g strawberries
2 tsp ground almonds
200ml semi-skimmed milk
toasted flaked almonds, to garnish

Purée the strawberries, ground almonds and milk in a blender or food processor until smooth. Serve chilled, garnished with the toasted flaked almonds.

Orange Citrus Fizz

**50MG VITAMIN C • 0MG BETA–CAROTENE •
0MG VITAMIN E • 33 CALORIES**

Serves 1

100ml freshly squeezed ruby-red orange juice
1 tbsp lemon juice
1 tbsp lime juice
100ml chilled sparkling mineral water

Stir together the juices and the mineral water. Serve with the slice of lemon and crushed ice.

CONVERSION CHART

All the calculations in this book for vitamins C, E and beta-carotene have been worked out using the metric measurements provided in the recipes. A conversion chart is provided here if you prefer to use Imperial measurements.

1 ounce is equivalent to 28g.

It's easier to round this down and call 1oz, 25g. By doing this the following measurements can be used.

1oz	=	25g	9oz	=	250g
2oz	=	50g	10oz	=	275g
3oz	=	75g	11oz	=	300g
4oz	=	125g	12oz	=	350g
5oz	=	150g	13oz	=	375g
6oz	=	175g	14oz	=	400g
7oz	=	200g	15oz	=	425g
8oz	=	225g	1lb	=	450g

Fluids

1 pint	=	600ml
¾ pint	=	450ml
½ pint	=	300ml
¼ pint	=	150ml

INDEX